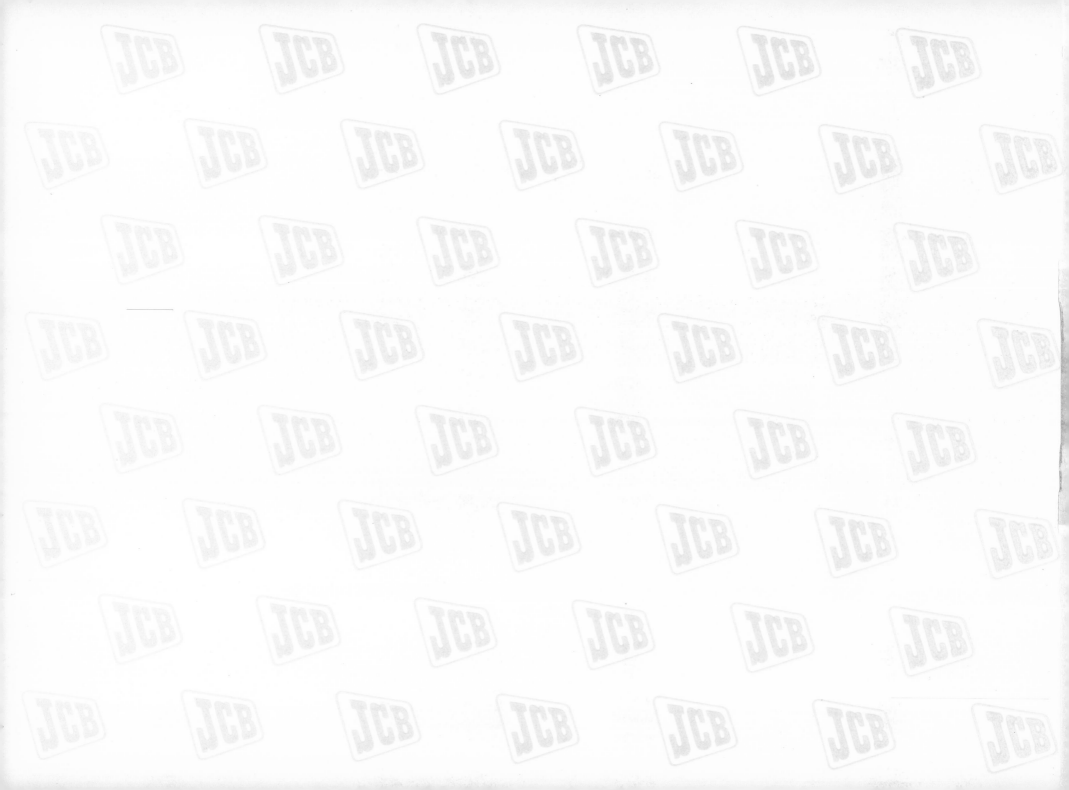

THE FIRST FIFTY YEARS

1945 ~ 1995

SPECIAL EVENT BOOKS

About the author
John Mitchell has 25 years experience of writing about British industry. He worked at JCB from 1977 to 1989 and therefore knows the company well. Today he is a freelance writer and industrial television producer.

Edited by
Michael Hancock,
director of public relations,
J C Bamford Excavators Ltd.

© Special Event Books in association with JC Bamford Excavators Ltd.

Designed by Barry O'Dwyer

First edition May 1995

ISBN 0 9516530 6 7

Special Event Books an imprint of
Open Eye Publishing
18 City Business Centre
Brighton Road
Horsham
West Sussex
England

Tel 01403 274598
Fax 01403 274599

CONTENTS

4

FOREWORD

*This book tells the story of the first 50 years of JCB.
It provides an insight into the early pioneering days that
led to the company becoming one of Britain's
great success stories.*

*The purpose of those early days was the same as it is
today; to make the best even better.*

*Fifty years on, engineering excellence and innovation remain
the hallmarks of JCB and our company has
become a world force in the construction equipment industry.*

*This book is dedicated with heartfelt thanks to all who have been
associated with JCB over the years; employees, suppliers,
distributors and most importantly the customers without whom
this success story could not be told.*

AP Bamford

JC Bamford

INTRODUCTION

A manufacturer's first duty is to make profit to survive and grow. Sometimes this may become separated from the duty of leadership, which is to add something extra for the benefit of the final inspector - the customer.

At JCB, profit, survival and growth have never been separated from adding benefit for the customer.

It is this spirit which makes a study of the first fifty years so important for the future. This is a message for anyone who cares to listen.

This is not a cold listing of dates and obsolete model names and numbers. It is a story of single minded determination to succeed, of willingness to put the company first. It is a tribute to Joe Bamford's foresight and development work, and Anthony Bamford's nurturing of the company into a much larger enterprise with diverse strengths and promise.

It is also a story of achievement by a team of people who always find challenge exhilarating.

CHAPTER ONE

The building of a legend

How it all began

Today JCB's modern complex seems so very far from its spartan beginnings. There is a famous story of the impresario who turned down The Beatles for a recording contract believing they wouldn't get very far. There is also a lesser known story of a finance house which noted in its card indexed records in the early fifties that young Mr J C Bamford had "little chance of expansion".

Years earlier his uncle Henry, who ran the family-owned agricultural engineering company Bamfords Ltd in Uttoxeter, had presumably thought along similar lines when he wrote him a note saying his services would no longer be required.

Joe Bamford rented a lock-up garage for 30 shillings a week. He was later to make his first investment - one pound on a second-hand welding set - only to find that, because of continuing wartime restrictions it would be useless at the time. The garage had no electricity. But later this welding set was to be invaluable. It now takes pride of place in the reception foyer of the Rocester factory complex.

Now many run their hands over it, and hope it will bring them luck.

Joe Bamford opened for business on 23 October 1945, the day his first son Anthony was born. So he had a wife and child, and no money; and that situation, in his own words "tended to concentrate my mind".

His first product was a farm trailer built largely from wartime scrap. Painted, with coachlines and his signature added, it appeared for sale at £90 in Uttoxeter market.

On the third Wednesday of showing it sold for £45 and the buyer's old cart was taken in part exchange. After renovating it and adding a fresh coat of paint and some coachlines, Joe returned to the market a week later and sold that one for another £45. He had made his original asking price.

From a small garage to one of Europe's most admired manufacturing facilities. For 18 months Joe Bamford rented a garage opposite the cinema in Uttoxeter for about 30 shillings a week. The area measured 12ft x 15ft where he worked mostly alone until he was asked to leave. The owner did not approve of Sunday working. The garage was demolished in 1969 with a JCB 6C. A replica now stands near the Sports and Social Club bowling green at Rocester. Lakeside Works, Rocester, is considered by many to be the finest engineering factory in Europe. The site covers 71 hectares (175 acres) and covered factory area exceeds 112,000 sq. m (1.2m sq. ft)

During 1946 he handled almost every job himself including cutting, forming and welding. By this time electricity had been connected. Unable to afford a drilling machine he contracted this out to a local bus garage and finally employed Harold Foster part-time in the evening to do painting jobs.

With business looking up Joe was working an energetic seven day week by early 1947. But his landlady disapproved of Sunday working and so he transferred to a section of the stabling and coachouse block at Crakemarsh Hall midway between Uttoxeter and Rocester. He was about to become a full time employer for the first time.

Joe and Anthony Bamford with the company's first product, a screw tipping farm trailer made in 1945 by Mr Bamford mainly from war surplus materials. Tyres and axle are original, taken from an old Albion truck. It is the only one ever made with wooden side boards, all others were steel. Almost all welding in the early years was stick welded on Mr Bamford's portable English Electric machine, which he bought second-hand for £1 in October 1945.

Arthur, Bert , Bill and John

In the early spring of 1947 fourteen year old Bill Hirst went to the Uttoxeter labour exchange looking for a job. He had wanted to stay on at St Joseph's Uttoxeter where he had been head boy. But as the youngest of nine money was needed, and therefore Bill found himself that next day in April a two mile bike ride from his Rocester home at the stables of Crakemarsh Hall. Inside the office, the old tack room , was 33 year old Joe Bamford.

To his left a small window looked into the 40 foot by 18 foot welding shop. "So he could look up and make sure we were all working," says Bill.

Bill was introduced to employee number one Arthur 'Pom Pom' Harrison, who had earlier worked with Joe Bamford at English Electric, Stafford.

He was interviewed, and set on as 'can lad' - tea boy - by welder Bert Holmes. Thus as employee number three, Bill Hirst began work at JCB. At Crakemarsh, Arthur and Bert built trailers to Joe Bamford's instructions. 'Pom Pom' Harrison with the hand operated pillar drill and the electric 'donkey' saw was the machine shop, cutting and drilling the components that would turn ex War Department parts into farm trailers. With Joe Bamford's welding set and a pair of axle stands Bert was the welding and assembly department. Bill biked it from Rocester, and for £1 a week discovered what hard work was all about.

Meanwhile, less than a mile away a hard working 21 year old farm contractor had bought a Ford tractor and Ransomes plough from his former boss to have a go at being self employed. Young John Wheeldon worked the farms between Uttoxeter and Alton with his Ford tractor and Ransomes plough.

This 1947 picture shows Mr Bamford with two year old Anthony and one of the company's all-steel tipping trailers. The wheel and tyres are from a Grumman Hellcat fighter aircraft, the hubs are from a small howitzer, and welded to a 4 in x 3 in RSJ which serves as the axle. The point here is simplicity, a watchword in the coming years. Apprentice Bill Hirst is on the left. Bill retired as director of international service standards in 1991 in his 45th year with JCB. Next to Bill is the late Arthur Harrison who as first foreman ran the machine shop. Next to Mr JCB is the late Bert Holmes, the first welder.

When John decided to buy himself a trailer it was to Joe Bamford he went. And it was to him that Joe Bamford delivered several days later a new screw-tipping trailer.

John Wheeldon: "I was one of Mr Bamford's earliest customers. So he then sent other customers to see me. He would say, go and see what big loads he is carrying. Many is the time would- be customers would come to ask what I thought of JCB trailers."

And so it was that John Wheeldon began as ambassador for JCB. Today customer endorsement is classic marketing technique. But here in 1947 was the earliest recorded example of Mr Bamford's intuitive sales style.

Joe Bamford (left) and Bert Holmes (centre) and John Hodgkinson with a screw jack trailer manufactured at Crakemarsh stables during a period when materials were in very short supply. Corrugated air-raid shelters were rolled flat to 6ft x 3ft by metal merchants in Bilston and then cut to form the front board and two side boards. On the right is the old saddle room which housed the machine shop.

Young John Wheeldon was to meet tough times. Tractors had been on restricted allocation. But when supplies increased tractors became readily available from manufacturers and also War Department sales. John's customers began buying their own. The bottom dropped out of John's market. He sold his tractor and plough. His JCB trailer made £100 at Uttoxeter Market, the same price he had paid for it new two years earlier.

Later he was to join Mr Bamford at Crakemarsh. And so John Wheeldon, as employee number six following Herbert Tickhill and Hilary 'Squinner' Brown joined JCB in August 1948. He was now working for the man who had sold him the trailer back in 1946. John: "Mr Bamford said that I could join as a general hand but I would have to learn to weld and he would teach me. He did too."

John Wheeldon knew the agricultural scene, the focus of the company's business in the early years. He also had experience of

construction from work on airfields such as Darley Moor, several army camps and the airfield at Derby Road, Ashbourne. Long after the airfield ceased most of the land would be bought years later by the company for use as its demonstration ground.

Now able to expand, production of single and twin axle drawbar trailers continued by the use of salvage materials.

The First Hydraulics

Expansion also meant diversification, with an entry into the commercial vehicle market. Joe acquired ex-Service vehicles; mainly Jeeps, vans and trucks, often still in their packing cases, and refurbished them for general haulage operations.

With a general shortage of transport vehicles Joe saw a ready market for the large number of ex-W.D. Jeeps, ambulances, command cars and RAF articulated trailers, all suitably converted.

The first tipping trailer had a manually operated screw device. The first JCB machine to utilise a hydraulic system as a means of movement was an agricultural trailer. Produced in 1948 it was possibly the world's - certainly Europe's - first two-wheeled, hydraulic, all-steel tipping trailer. Life was made easier for the operator with tipping operation possible from the tractor seat.

However no one had yet devised a double acting ram. The trailers would tip up but it was then necessary to drive half way round a field so that the trailer bed would lower itself down again. Ford made the first tractors available in the UK with hydraulic take-off. This was achieved by taking out the rear axle plug and coupling up to a steel pipe, then a short hose into the hydraulic ram.

Ford were later to offer two options, either the tractor's own hydraulics or with a Varley gear type pump. This was later to be used on the first Major Loaders.

At this time farmers were still loading trailers by hand, and it was this which led to thoughts of utilising hydraulics for a loader, in order to load trailers. Mr Bamford used his knowledge of hydraulics in aircraft landing gear. The Major Loader was the result.

But there was competition; a loader attachment made by Midland Industries Ltd and also a muck loader, the Horndraulic, made by Steel Fabrications, Cardiff, under licence from the American company Horn. It was whilst on a competitive demonstration at Market Harborough that John Wheeldon had a taste of Mr Bamford's foresight.

John: "They had single acting hydraulic rams, we had single acting rams, but later that night in a small hotel Mr Bamford was drawing some sketches and then he suddenly said 'what we need is a double acting ram so you can put a down pressure on it'. There were no double acting rams, they didn't exist. I was really surprised."

However it was not until 1953, four years later, that double acting rams were first used on the MK1 excavator.

The Major Loader was the first European hydraulic loader, introduced in 1948 and sold for about £110. It was named the Major Loader as early development work was carried out on the Fordson Major - the most popular tractor of the time. Sold in kit form, either for mounting by the farmer or by dealers, it was later developed for mounting on all popular makes of tractor and thousands were sold. Attachments included a muck fork, bag lift and crane arm.

A wave from Anthony Bamford, the little boy standing on the gatepost next to his father, in front of the old cheese factory about 1951. The Austin A40 pick up was often driven by Mrs Marjorie Bamford to collect components from suppliers in the Birmingham area. The building's ground floor metal windows were all made at the factory, replacing old wooden windows which had mostly rotted away.

1948. Road vehicles like this Jeep were bought as ex-war surplus either new in packing cases or with under 100 miles on the clock. They were painted white and weather protection added. This Jeep is about to deliver a new single axle hydraulic tipping trailer. With his aviator's certificate awarded in June 1948 Mr Bamford also bought and re-furnished aircraft for resale. Profits went straight back into the business.

The Si-draulic was a simple bolt on kit for tractors and sold for £75. This single arm design was a world first. Around 6,000 were made by JCB and 20,000 under licence in France, where this picture was taken.

In late 1950 JCB outgrew the stables at Crakemarsh and bought the old Wiltshire United Dairies milk processing and cheese factory at Rocester from farmer John Bailey. John Wheeldon was linked yet again, for he had worked for Bailey and then bought his tractor and plough.

Even in the very earliest days of John Wheeldon's 42 years with the company he recognised that there was something special about the JCB way of working.

Mr Bamford set Pom Pom Harrison's productivity as an example to John Wheeldon. Pom Pom, so nicknamed because he was an accomplished pianist, arranged his work such that he could do four or five jobs at the same time.

He expected as much from others. Sometimes when the welding shop went quiet Pom Pom would tip toe across and lift the latch to the stable door to spy on Bill Hirst and see what he was up to. Inventiveness took many forms at Crakemarsh, as Pom Pom discovered to his cost. Bill and his mates used to run hidden fuse wire to the door latch and connect it back to a steel bench. Then by completing the circuit with the welding set's electrode they would nip away to watch Pom Pom get an electric shock as he lifted the door latch.

Bill: "While he was leaping about we got back to work and disconnected the electrode. He used to swear that door was live but he never cottoned on ".

Alec Hollingworth operating a Si-draulic on ground now built-up as O Bay. This was very boggy ground which Bill Hirst discovered to his cost when he drove a tractor across it one day and became stuck. He spent the whole of the next weekend digging the tractor out.

Incredible as it may seem today, the huge Rocester complex is only there because of Bill Hirst and his bicycle. When Mr Bamford had the Dodge truck and Pom Pom had a car, Bill Hirst was still having to cycle in from Rocester. Joe Bamford, being a Uttoxeter man, was looking for better premises over Uttoxeter way.

Bill Hirst: "I knew John Bailey was thinking of selling the old cheese factory and I persuaded Joe to buy it. I thought it was great because now I only had to get up at one minute to eight instead of ten to eight. So that's how we came to be at Rocester, it was because I didn't want to bike such a long way into work."

Bill was able to get rid of his battered old bicycle. He was coming up in the world.

Bill: "I bought Joe Bamford's three-speed bicycle for £9 and paid it off at two and sixpence a week. It was great, it was much better than mine."

The move to Rocester was provoked partly by complaints about Sunday working at Crakemarsh by the owner Mrs Cavendish. It was reminiscent of earlier complaints about the same thing in the old garage at Uttoxeter. Here at Rocester, they could work as long as they liked.

Mr Bamford's office at the new Lakeside Works was converted from a deep litter chicken run. Over three inches of chicken droppings had to be cleaned from the floor and the smell lingered for months. When the earthworks were finished the site covered just under one acre. It was around this time that the green paintwork on JCB machines and trailers was changed to the distinctive bright yellow, which has since become so familiar a sight.

The Major Loader of 1949, so called because it was designed primarily around the Fordson Major, although also fitted to the Nuffield as shown here. It was Europe's first hydraulic heavy duty front end loader. This new wonder of hydraulic power was at the time only applied in farming, here demonstrated about 1951 by lifting an entire tractor. Note the hay swath bar which carries the earliest elements of the famous JCB logo.

John Wheeldon driving a Major Loader. He was in charge of the first operator training done on this ground in the early fifties. Operator training began with manufacturing of the first excavator in 1953. This photo of a Major Loader shows a front shovel fitted, although the first attachment produced was a muck fork to save farmers having to load trailers by hand. The Major Loader frame fitted around the tractor. The shovel was tripped by a claw device which gripped a bar until opened by levers and a wire rope. These were the days of basic trial and error.

Finding the customers

Throughout this time and in the days to come, Mrs Marjorie Bamford, sometimes known as Meggi, played a large part in the company's development. She took Anthony on frequent trips in his carrycot in an Austin A40 pick-up to Birmingham and the Black Country to collect paint, spare parts and components. Mrs Bamford was also involved at the various shows around the country. A small caravan was bought for office and customer reception purposes.

She would get up early during exhibitions to bake and prepare sandwiches. At one exhibition Mr JCB had black and white leaflets printed which he asked Mrs Bamford to distribute to likely looking customers. She managed to present one, unknown to her, to one of the Whitlock brothers, major competitors. They complained to the organisers, saying that JCB was taking an unfair advantage over other exhibitors. By that time the JCB stand was full of enthusiastic potential customers.

For 1951 JCB announced the Master Loader, a smaller version of the Major Loader made especially for loading muck into farm carts, trailers and spreaders. At £75 complete, some 2,000 were sold.

One of the development projects brought

A Si-draulic and Loadover at an agricultural exhibition 1953. The Si-draulic was only ever made with a muck fork. Both machines were of tubular construction, and therefore torsionally stable.

from Crakemarsh was a mid-mounted mower. This allowed the operator to see the cut being made directly to the side, instead of having to look over the shoulder as with towed alternatives.

With its German Busatis cutter bar the mid mower would be left running, connected to an electric motor in the 'test bed' temporary Nissen hut. Many times Alec Hollingworth, who lived nearby, would hear banging and clattering from his test bed rig in the middle of the night and go running down to sort the problem, only to be covered in oil.

The JCB mid mounted mower worked very well and was manufactured for two years after which the rights were sold to Bamfords Ltd.

John Wheeldon : "They put their own cutter bar on. But I consider the Busatis cutter bar was better due to being of more modern design."

1953 was a turning point for JCB with a world first in the shape of the Si-draulic Loader. It was to remain for many years the only loader mounted on one side of a tractor with the forks centrally positioned and it offered high lift and good forward reach unattainable by any of its competitors. Value for money at £75, some 6,000 were made by JCB and a further 20,000 under licence in France.

Fun at the Royal Show, 1953. In the shovel of the Loadover are (left) Doug Hollingworth an agricultural contractor who helped set up some of the shows; Mr Bamford's first full-time secretary Margaret Wood who joined at Crakemarsh; JCB's first sales manager Jim Titley who travelled extensively for the company in the early fifties. An electrician by trade, Jim joined JCB full time after installing the first three-phase power into Rocester at night with John Wheeldon. Identity of the two boys unknown. Note strong use of the company name, a pointer for the future.

It was designed by Mr Bamford to be simple to make. The arm could be detached from the tractor in about ten minutes, which would leave the rear of the trailer and the drawbar clear for operating other hydraulic implements. A shut-off valve diverted the oil from the Si-draulic ram to vertical lift implements.

Sometimes in engineering design failures can be more interesting than the successes, and so it is with the JCB Loadover. In order to save time in the loading cycle, the loader bucket was designed to travel over the top of the driver and be dumped at the rear.

The Loadover was most significant as it was the first machine to bear the 'JCB' logo. Only two were made. The tubular frame was used as hydraulic reservoir, an idea picked up later in the design of the JCB Hydra-Chassis on backhoe loaders.

The Loadover required a special technique for lowering the shovel and discharging into the truck. It was done by lifting the arms up to top dead centre whilst moving forward and then the hydraulic lever was switched to the opposite direction. The arms would then descend to discharge the load.

Without this knowledge it was easy to have a full shovel sticking straight up in the air going nowhere.

The Loadover has great historical significance as the first product to carry the fully recognisable JCB logo. It is also interesting because the hydraulic oil reservoir, believed to be about 75 gallon capacity, was the inside of the 6 inch tubular frame. This pre-dates the 1957 Hydra-Digga which employed the same reservoir idea, and also the 3C of 1963 which heavily promoted the Hydra-Chassis concept.

The Loadover, named in a works competition, saved turning during the loading operation. The shovel was filled with the arms flat over the back wheels and then lifted over the driver's canopy to be dumped into trucks or rail wagons as shown here in Uttoxeter gas works. The driver is John Wheeldon. Only two were made. One went to ICI Chemicals at Speke and the fate of the other is unknown. The single acting rams required a special technique, which was to use inertia to carry the shovel over top dead centre whilst the direction level was quickly engaged into the 'lower' position.

In these vital days of trial and error much was learned.

Bill Hirst: "In the earliest days the back axle of the tractor was the reservoir for the hydraulic oil, which was just thick axle oil. On the first Major Loader we built, the arms would not lift beyond the horizontal. We couldn't figure out why. Then we realised it had taken all the oil out of the back axle. This was all magical pioneering stuff."

"Then we built a small reservoir which held about a gallon of oil which we bolted to the hydraulic unit on the tractor. We filled that up and lo and behold it took the arms right to the top. Then when the arms came down the pressure blew the reservoir right off the tractor. We had forgotten that we had filled the reservoir to the top when the system was half full to start with."

The Major Loader, later the High Speed Major Loader, was significant because it marked the first move into muckshifting as distinct from agriculture, JCB's first market. One a day was built between 1949 and 1956.

It had a Plessey pump fitted to the crankshaft, which improved performance and speed. This was a significant improvement. JCB was leading the field with a development which took the company into construction rather than pure agricultural applications.

With the High Speed, JCB was beginning to move away from tractor hydraulics. There was a pump and a valve block and a separate circuit and hydraulic tank bolted to the side of the frame. This is where it began to take off as a loading shovel rather than a farm implement because customers realised it could handle some tough work.

Bill joined the army in 1951 on National Service and served with the Royal Military Police in Kenya during the Mau-Mau uprising. In his spare time he kept an eye on JCB machines working there, and remained in contact with Mr JCB. When he returned to Rocester in 1953 he was made foreman welder. JCB had grown to employ about 35 people.

The address of the new factory was Lakeside Works, Rocester, and it still is to this day. Many believe this is because of the lakes surrounding the factory, but not so. Lakeside Works originally referred to the lake at Crakemarsh. The lakes at Rocester were not dug until the sixties.

At Rocester, Alf Bettany and his wife Winnie lived in the bungalow next door, and she began making tea for some of the workers when they had no facilities. Later she and Mrs Oliver from the station crossing house nearby used to go into the factory to sell sweets, tea and chocolate.

Alf: "I was going in one Sunday morning and Joe stopped me and apologised for all the activity and said he hoped that the factory wasn't being a nuisance to us. He also said that one day there would be a job for me here if I wanted one."

Alf worked at JCB for 25 years full time and his wife worked there too. So did his brother Denis and other members of the family. There were to be many other Rocester families who all contributed much to JCB over the years.

It was a visit by Mr Bamford to Norway that really marked the starting point for enormous success to come. On a mission to sell JCB half tracks, Joe noticed something new - a lightweight hydraulic backhoe which so caught his attention he bought one. The potential did not escape him even though the machine built by Eik Hauskins Co was very restricted and would only slew to about 80 degrees from the centre line.

After shipping the machine back to England, it was examined in the workshop. The conclusion was soon reached that there was something here, and JCB would be able to build a better one.

Lessons learned were put to work in designing and producing JCB's first backhoe - the MK 1. Based on the Fordson Major Tractor, it cost £1,300 as a dealer fit. Joe Bamford soon realised a Major Loader could also be fitted at the front, providing a far more versatile tool.

This is how Europe's first backhoe loader was born. From the start the MK 1 was fitted to a tractor along with the Major Loader. A counterweight option was available for customers who did not require a MK 1 but this was frowned upon by Mr Bamford who would always try to encourage dealers to sell the backhoe and loader combination. The MK 1 hydraulic system worked at a pressure of 1250 psi, a far cry from the 4000 psi pressures of today.

The Rocester site in 1950, covering just under one acre. Note the JCB trailer, as well as Fordson and Nuffield tractors. The building with the tiled roof is the former cheese factory and milk collection centre for local farmers. The building with the domed roof is the main structure of the first Rocester factory, actually a six-bay Dutch hay barn erected by farmer John Bailey in 1946 as a cattle sale yard, an unsuccessful venture which led to the sale of the site to Mr Bamford. The concrete rollers in the foreground are wartime tank traps which guarded Whites Bridge, Rocester, over the River Churnet.

It must be remembered just how revolutionary the JCB MK I was. Before this, the closest was the Ruston Bucyrus 10RB, a machine designed for the quarry face. This depended on the boom weight and cables alone. It was not really a digger.

Bill Hirst: "At the time hydraulics had not been developed. Nobody knew about the incredible force that could be generated. Now we take it all for granted."

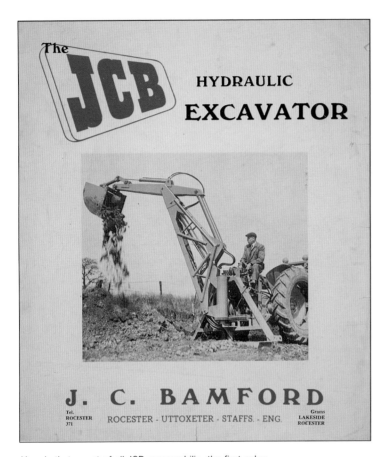

The JCB HYDRAULIC EXCAVATOR

J. C. BAMFORD

Tel.
ROCESTER
371

ROCESTER - UTTOXETER - STAFFS. - ENG.

Grams
LAKESIDE
ROCESTER

HYDRAULIC EXCAVATOR
SPECIFICATION

SYSTEM	Totally hydraulic.
PUMP	Special design with self-aligning pressure sealing protected by filter unit.
SCOOP SIZES	10in. to 48in. all with replaceable manganese digging teeth and cutters.
CYLINDERS	Precision ground with chromed pistons to eliminate wear and damage due to climatic conditions.
OPERATING VALVES	Total of 5 valves employed for operation giving swing, boom, lift, digging and bucket crowd. Each valve is protected by individual overload protection.
OPERATIONAL SPEED	15 to 45 cubic yards per hour.
BOOM	This can be swivelled and will dig over a full 180°.
PRICE	As per Quotation Ex-Works for Fordson Major (new type).
DEPTH	11ft. 0ins.
HEIGHT	12ft. 0ins.
REACH	15ft. 0ins.

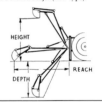

Here is that rarest of all JCB memorabilia, the first sales leaflet for a JCB Mk 1 hydraulic excavator. This is the excavator of 1953 with tubular boom construction. Later models switched to channel construction. The 180 degree slew arc was Mr Bamford's answer to farmers' demands for a machine which could run parallel to ditch cleaning. His earlier protoypes with 90 degrees slew could not. When the answer struck him at a farming exhibition Joe telephoned chief designer Alec Kelly ordering him to torch the 90 degree models and start again; blinding inspiration but huge risk for the fledgling company.

This leaflet focuses on the excavator and its 'A' frame stabiliser. The front loader is shown without any dump mechanism to the front shovel, neither is it fitted with a shovel or muck fork. But the future backhoe loader is plain to see.

Rare leaflet kindly loaned by Mr John Wheeldon, the operator in the picture.

There are more surprises in looking back, for on the first Mk 1 Major Loaders it was not possible to operate the front end and back end at the same time. It was necessary to take a pipe from the valve block at the back having first raised the back end up to gain access. The pipe then had to be threaded underneath the machine to the front valve block.

Bill Hirst: "And this went on for years and people loved it, they thought it was wonderful. Remember few people had ever dug a trench before other than with a hand shovel."

There were to be many technical problems to overcome, chiefly to do with such natural phenomena as induced pressures and cavitation. Mr Bamford's workers were given rewards for their ideas, a tradition which still holds good today.

One of Bill Hirst's suggestions was the principle of the double shafted slew ram whereby there is equal displacement either side of the ram head allowing oil to be dumped from side to side to stop cavitation on the slew mechanism. Bill Hirst moved from foreman welder into the research department to develop ideas. He retired as director of international service standards in 1991 in his 45th year with the company.

Before production ceased in 1957 over 200 MK 1's had been sold; success based on unique versatility and strength. Chassis number 2126 highlights this. Sold in 1954 to Derby Co-op for operation in their coal yard, sorting and loading coal, it was finally pensioned off in 1967, 13 years later.

The operator took some lengthy persuading to part with it, but finally agreed when he found that the replacement JCB 3D came with an electric kettle. He was tickled pink with the idea of brewing his own tea and travelled daily to Rocester to view his machine going down the production line.

The earliest surviving photograph of the Rocester production line. Major Loaders in 1956.

The breakthroughs continue

Another major breakthrough came in 1957 with the arrival of the JCB Hydra-Digga. Larger and more powerful than any preceding JCB machine, it was advertised as the earthmover that could dig through rock. This is regarded by many as the true commercial beginning of JCB.

Further development in 1958 produced the Loadall, with a solidly engineered front loader designed to fit Fordson and Ferguson tractors.

In the earliest years Mr Bamford traded as J.C. Bamford, Agricultural Engineers, Lakeside Works. At the foot of the firm's headed paper were the words: 'Not To Be Confused With Any Other Company Of The Same Name'. The certificate of incorporation as J.C. Bamford (Excavators) Ltd was granted in February 1956. The famous JCB logo is actually registered as Trademark Number B773566 dated 25th January 1958. On 1st May 1967 the Board's minutes show the name was changed to J C Bamford Excavators Limited.

The formation of JCB as a registered company in 1956 coincided with the creation of a service department, Rocester Services Ltd in March. The MK 1 was updated considerably with the help of the first service manager Paul Marvin.

With an improved front loader and more powerful backhoe, the Hydra-Digga Loadall was the first model to provide the operator with a comfortable cab, complete with heater. Here was the start of JCB attention to operator comfort. Over 2,000 were sold before production ceased in 1960.

The Hydra-Digga of 1957, named after Greek mythology by Mrs Marjorie Bamford, had a larger boom and dipper than the MK 1. It was available with or without a Major Loader. In 1958 the Loadall with integral hydra-chassis oil reservoir for the innovative hydraulic shovel was introduced.

Together these two became the Hydra-Digga Loadall and the recognisable style of a backhoe loader had arrived. The chassis took digging and loading forces, not the tractor skid. This Loadall 65 is outside the design department in 1959.

For the remainder of the 1950's Mr Bamford concentrated on developing his company, expanding the factory and creating a more efficient dealer network. As now, profit was pumped directly back into the business.

More power and sophistication was built into the JCB 4, which replaced the Hydra-Digga Loadall in 1960 and featured for the first time in a JCB, dual hydraulics, the innovative 3-in-1 backhoe bucket and now familiar JCB two-lever excavator control system.

1961 was momentous. The JCB 3 was unveiled, and with thousands of improvements over the coming years it continued to be improved until 1980, when the 3CX backhoe loader was introduced. The JCB 3 was a real trend-setter, smaller and more compact than the JCB 4, and designed specifically for the house builder rather than civil engineering. The JCB 3 had independent twin vertical stabilisers, a lower centre of gravity and a sliding kingpost, which enabled the machine to dig tight up alongside walls or other obstructions. The backhoe operated through 180 degrees. For the operator there was a swivel seat for front or rear end work.

An improved version of the JCB 4, the 4C, was introduced in 1962. A completely new machine, it extended performance.

A Hydra-Digga Loadall 65 fitted with bulldozer blade at work on new factory groundworks in 1959. The dipper had two sets of holes for either power or speed positions. Also the boom had a long ram, very different to the short ram of the earlier Mk 1. The Hydra-Digga was an extremely powerful digger which really put JCB into the construction market. Note clear evidence of JCB's determination to grow; the existing factory bay stanchions were built ready to take the next roof span without further expense.

The JCB 4 of 1960 pioneered the first two-lever JCB cross pattern excavator control developed with Hamworthy Hydraulics. For the first time the operator could control all excavating functions with his hands on two levers at all times. This was impossible with the earlier five lever value block. Aimed at public works contractors the 4 had 19ft reach. The spacious JCB Superview cab made the 4 a popular site vehicle able to carry several people.

18 degrees to the horizontal

Few corporate logos enjoy instant public recognition. Yet the JCB logo is universally known. It is a vigorously guarded mark, first registered under the 1938 Trade Marks Act on 25 January 1958, and now covered in over 700 registrations worldwide.

Today the company issues strict rules to distributors, insisting it must not be changed or distorted in any way. Instructions cover how it may be used and in which colours. Whilst every aspect is guarded it is the so called 'angle of dangle' which is quoted most. This is the angle between the lowest straight border and an imaginary horizontal. Stories abound of Mr Bamford suddenly quizzing aspiring executives on the angle of dangle. The wise memorise 18 degrees to the horizontal.

The JCB logo was produced originally because he wanted to avoid confusion with the old family firm Bamfords Ltd in nearby Uttoxeter. The shape was developed by a small design agency in Wolverhampton, closely following the J.C . Bamford sign on a 1951 hay mower side swath bar. The first product to bear the logo was the Loadover of 1953, followed by the boom of the Mk 1 excavator in 1954.

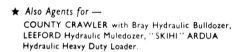

Here are some interesting examples of the increasing use of the logo in dealer advertising during the fifties. Advertising showed machines working, such as the Mk 1 trenching and loading the lorry from O'Dair Bros Ltd, of Tean in 1956. In these early years the concept of the hydraulic excavator had to be sold strongly, rather than by the brand which was expressed in a variety of ways. But as the years went by the importance of the logo grew. By the sixties it spearheaded brand recognition.

Manual typewriters and telex machines were fitted with special logo keys from about 1960 and through into the seventies, and this unique office practice continues to this day in the electronic age. Desktop PCs are now pre-formatted in Microsoft Office software so that JCB logos may be selected from a menu for faxes or memos.

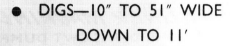

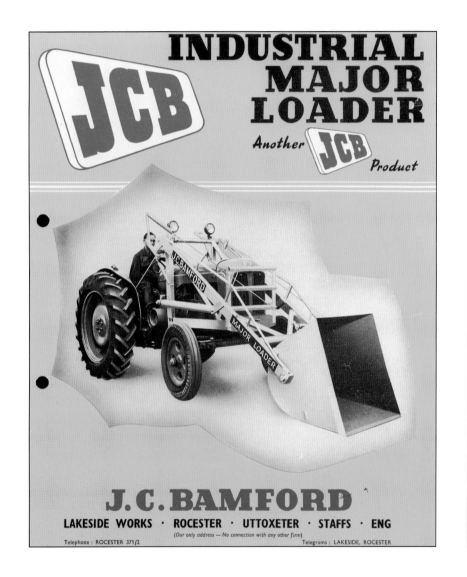

INDUSTRIAL MAJOR LOADER

JCB

Another **JCB** *Product*

J. C. BAMFORD

LAKESIDE WORKS · ROCESTER · UTTOXETER · STAFFS · ENG

(Our only address — No connection with any other firm)

Telephone : ROCESTER 371/2   Telegrams : LAKESIDE, ROCESTER

BULLDOZER BLADE ATTACHMENT

NUFFIELD MODEL WITH 15 CWT. CRANE

GENERAL PURPOSE BUCKET

★ IT LOADS ★
IT LIFTS
★
IT PUSHES ★
IT SCOOPS
★
IT SCRAPES ★
★ IT BULLDOZES

J.C.B. INDUSTRIAL MAJOR LOADER

SPECIFICATION

(Patents Pending)

SUBFRAME. Fits all Fordson Major Tractors and may be left permanently in position. Also available for the Nuffield Universal.

JIB. This is of welded one-piece construction and consequently can withstand all stresses and cannot work loose. Side members are rolled steel channel, boxed and braced with tie rods and braced together with heavy tubular cross members. Fitted to the subframe in one minute.

CYLINDERS. Massive twin cylinders of patented design give perfect balanced lift. For special duties other larger cylinders are available.

WHEELS. 750 × 16 8-ply Front Wheel equipment strongly recommended.

ATTACHMENTS

GENERAL PURPOSE BUCKET. Suitable for digging all materials. ⅜ cu. yd. capacity. 12 ft. 9 maximum height. 8 ft. 0 ins. under lip when tipped. Minimum tip height 1 ft. 6 ins. Heavily constructed of ¼" steel plate, well ribbed, and has renewable wearing parts.

BULLDOZER. This enables all loose or light soils, etc., to be easily bulldozed and is readily attached. It is particularly suitable for site clearing and back filling trenches.

BALLAST BLOCK. Weighs 15 cwt. and is strongly advised as it increases traction and stability, also includes heavy duty draw bar.

HIGH SPEED PUMP. Engine driven, giving speed of lift of seven seconds and should be used for all industrial applications in place of Fordson hydraulics.

CRANE. Lifts 15 cwts. to 10 ft. 6 ins.

JIB EXTENSION. For all lifting operations up to 17 ft. 8 cwts.

PLATFORM. Enables sacks, bricks, etc., to be delivered to an 11 ft. loft or staging and for a man to pick fruit or paint up to 18 ft. height.

HEAVY DUTY FORK. Specially designed for Farmyard Muck. Tines are renewable.

Advice given on any handling problems.

Specifications are given without commitment. J. C. Bamford reserve the right, in furtherance of the policy of constant development, to alter or amend any of the dimensions or particulars without notice.

PRICE LIST (Ex Works)

Major-Loader, all types	165.7.6	£157 10 0
Attachments :—		
General Purpose Bucket	33.1.6	£31 10 0
Bulldozer	68.5.4	£65 0 0
Platform	27.11.3	£26 5 0
Crane, 15 cwts.	18.14.9	£17 17 0
High Lift Jib	18.14.9	£17 17 0
Muck Fork	27.11.3	£26 5 0
3 Bucket Teeth	3.10.3.6	£5 0 0
Ballast Block	35.14.0	£34 0 0
(With extension draw bar)		
High Speed Pump	£121.5.6	£115 10 0
(Fordson pump not required)		
Cab (with wiper)	52.10	£50 0 0
750 × 16 Front Wheels and Tyres		£38 4 0

Note : A special bonnet hinge is necessary for servicing tractor on the Fordson (exchange bonnet system)   £5 5 0 / £5 0 0

Orders accepted on the basis of prices ruling on date of despatch.

EXPORT ENQUIRIES INVITED

Shipping singly approx. 9′ × 3′ × 4′ 6″—122 cu. ft. Weight 10·5 cwt. nett and gross.

— Also available for early delivery —

Side Mounted LOADERS, HALF TRACKS, Hydraulic EXCAVATORS

The Hydra-Digga price list of July 1957. Note that the company is no longer stressing agricultural engineering, and has changed its name to J.C. Bamford (Excavators) Ltd.

PRICE LIST

HYDRA-DIGGA AND MAJOR LOADER

with 750 x 16 front and 14 x 30 rear wheels and tyres, driver's cab, electric lighting and starting, handbrake, hour meter, ⅜ cu. yd. Loader Bucket, Bulldozer Blade and conversion operating valve, powered by the Fordson High Speed Diesel Engine.

Fitted at works, tested and with first filling of oil ...... **£1,890.5.6** Ex. Works

HYDRA-DIGGA AND BALLAST WEIGHT

with 750 x 16 front and 14 x 30 rear wheels and tyres, driver's cab, electric lighting and starting, handbrake and hour meter, powered by the Fordson High Speed Diesel Engine.

Fitted at works, tested and with first filling of oil ...... **£1,614.19.0** Ex. Works

(NO EXCAVATOR BUCKETS IN EITHER CASE)

Orders accepted on the basis of prices ruling on date of despatch

16th July, 1957.

J. C. BAMFORD (EXCAVATORS) LTD.

LAKESIDE WORKS, ROCESTER, UTTOXETER, STAFFS.

Telephone: ROCESTER 371   *Telegrams:* LAKESIDE, ROCESTER

BREAKDOWN PRICES and ADDITIONAL EQUIPMENT

HYDRA-DIGGA

	£	s.	d.
18—22 inch bucket	48	0	0
24—28 inch bucket	52	10	0
30—34 inch bucket	63	0	0
46—50 inch bucket	89	5	0
12—15 inch ejector bucket	65	0	0
Face Shovel Bucket	102	0	0
Ditching Bucket	55	0	0
Ditch Cleaning Blade	35	0	0
Ditching extension including hoses	45	0	0
Ballast Weight (when Loader not fitted)	20	0	0
Operator's Cab	52	10	0

MAJOR LOADER

	£	s.	d.
Major Loader, fitted complete with ⅜ cubic yard general purpose bucket including high speed pump	946	3	6
Ballast Weight (when Excavator not fitted)	35	14	0
Bulldozer Blade	68	5	0
High Speed Pump (Loader type only)	121	5	6
Conversion Operating Valve	23	12	6
(Enables the Loader to work off the Excavator High Speed Pump)			
Fordson Hydraulics and Power Take Off	65	10	0
(Can be used to operate the Loader, but we strongly recommend the use of the high speed pump as this speeds up the lift 100%)			
Bucket teeth (3) fitted	3	10	0
Bucket teeth loose	3	0	0
Crane (15 cwt.)	18	14	9
High Lift Jib	18	14	9

LOOSE MACHINES (for fitting to own tractor, crawler, etc.)

	£	s.	d.
J.C.B. Hydra-Digga	900	0	0
J.C.B. Major Loader	165	7	6
(Loader bucket—⅜ cubic yard)	33	1	6
Bonnet Hinge for Fordson Tractor	5	0	0

FITTING CHARGES

	£	s.	d.
J.C.B. HYDRA-DIGGA on Fordson Tractor	21	0	0
J.C.B. HYDRA-DIGGA on County Crawler	75	0	0
J.C.B. HYDRA-DIGGA on County Four Drive	75	0	0
J.C.B. HYDRA-DIGGA on Nuffield Tractor	31	0	0
J.C.B. MAJOR LOADER on Fordson or Nuffield Tractor	5	0	0

ALL PRICES GIVEN ARE EX. WORKS

SPECIFICATIONS ARE GIVEN WITHOUT COMMITMENT. J. C. BAMFORD (EXCAVATORS) LIMITED RESERVE THE RIGHT IN FURTHERANCE OF THE POLICY OF CONSTANT DEVELOPMENT, TO ALTER OR AMEND ANY OF THE DIMENSIONS OR PARTICULARS WITHOUT NOTICE.

P.L. 5/8/57   PRINTED IN ENGLAND

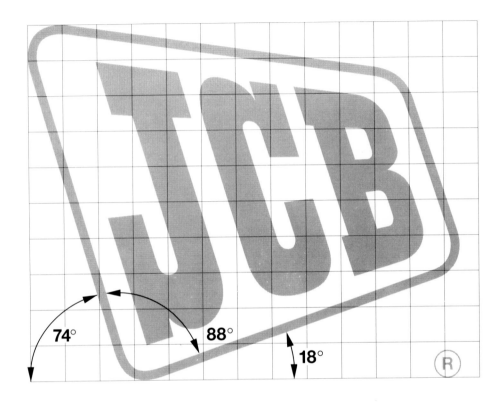

The 1963 logo had a 3D effect combined with a drop shadow. This was cleaned up and revised within the publicity department for 1972. In the mid eighties the shadow was removed.
Further revision has just taken place in 1995 to give a crisper look with less infill on the letter B. Various alterations were suggested including the angle of dangle. Surprise surprise, it is staying at 18 degrees.

By 1962 there had been considerable expansion. The cheese factory was the main office, the white building on the left was first a canteen, then the service training school run by Bill Hirst. The steel supports on the roof of the office block were installed to take a huge J C Bamford sign which was refused by local planners. The east drainage lake was later enlarged to form the first of the three lakes which are so admired today.

More pressure and more success

The sixties were the years of pressure and innovation at JCB.

In a short span the factory's greatest architectural advances were made. These were matched only by the greatest advances of all - changes to the architecture of the business itself.

The sixties brought the JCB 3C, the acknowledged design classic which changed thinking for ever.

But also the sixties tested the company's mettle to the maximum. There was a supplier's hydraulic seal failure which stopped JCB 4C production in 1962. Ford failed to meet supplies of skid units due to problems at Dagenham. The entire backhoe loader range had to be re-engined. The entire UK dealer network had to be overhauled virtually overnight.

Massive factory extensions were begun. The first machine was despatched to America. The company moved into hydraulic tracked excavators by a licensing deal with Warner Swasey for their Hopto machine which became the JCB 7. Chaseside Engineering was purchased for £823,000. And in the midst of all this Joe Bamford had yet another idea, an electric kettle.

Alan Cooper, appointed works director in 1964, remembers those times fondly ; 'You never knew what Joe Bamford would hit you with next. That was one of the joys of working here.'

The factory began producing the JCB 3C in March 1963. The machine was down to the sheer brilliance of the chief designer

A JCB 4 working in Japan in 1962. Exports have always been a very important part of JCB's history. In 1962 some 974 machines were exported out of 5,688 total deliveries.

Derek Prime, who packed it with innovations such as the rails by which the excavator assembly could slide sideways so the operator could always see clearly down a trench.

It was also the first machine with an integrated chassis which held the Ford skid unit. This was the first move away from bolt-ons to the tractor and therefore was a benchmark in design. It also had a bigger cab.

Derek Prime had worked on his design in spare moments and at nights. Mr Bamford and research director Alec Kelly had another concept with a knock-off excavator end, a machine similar to the JCB 4C but smaller. But when their design was discussed Derek pulled his own from a drawer and presented that too. Mr Bamford spotted the potential and put it into production in preference to his own.

The rest, as everyone in the construction industry will know, is history. The 3C took off, and took the company with it.

1962 factory production was 1,519 machines. With the 3C in 1963 production shot to 2,355, followed by 3,182 in 1964.

But in 1967 there came the 3D, an extended version of the 3C with a long dipper, big bucket on the front, and a mission to grab sales from the 4C without affecting the 3C.

One Saturday morning Mr Bamford called in his senior troops and asked each to come up with ideas on the 3D by Monday morning.

On the Monday morning Mr Bamford listened to all ideas, then leaned back with a broad grin on his face.

Alan Cooper remembers it all as if it were yesterday. "Nobody was really coming up with any decent suggestions, and Mr Bamford just sat there grinning that he had the answer. Then he said that it would be nice if the operator could make a cup of tea in the cab. He said that if the operator was happy and content he would stay in the cab instead of trudging across to the site hut, and if he was in the cab he would also be likely to do more work."

The JCB 4 was updated to the 4C in 1962 with a better cab and squared fender design. These machines used the hydra-chassis, but it was not yet totally complete; the rear 'A' frame was still linked to the tractor skid. This 4C was photographed in South Africa in 1965, and it is anyone's guess why the banksman is playing the flute.

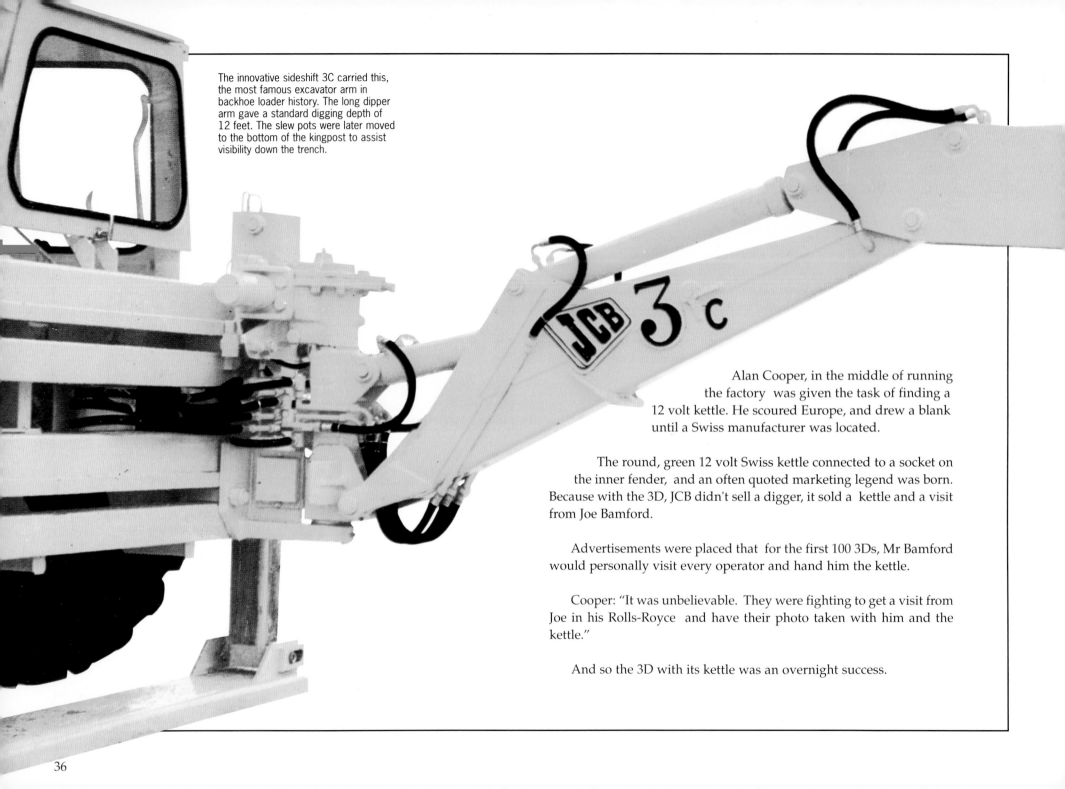

The innovative sideshift 3C carried this, the most famous excavator arm in backhoe loader history. The long dipper arm gave a standard digging depth of 12 feet. The slew pots were later moved to the bottom of the kingpost to assist visibility down the trench.

Alan Cooper, in the middle of running the factory was given the task of finding a 12 volt kettle. He scoured Europe, and drew a blank until a Swiss manufacturer was located.

The round, green 12 volt Swiss kettle connected to a socket on the inner fender, and an often quoted marketing legend was born. Because with the 3D, JCB didn't sell a digger, it sold a kettle and a visit from Joe Bamford.

Advertisements were placed that for the first 100 3Ds, Mr Bamford would personally visit every operator and hand him the kettle.

Cooper: "It was unbelievable. They were fighting to get a visit from Joe in his Rolls-Royce and have their photo taken with him and the kettle."

And so the 3D with its kettle was an overnight success.

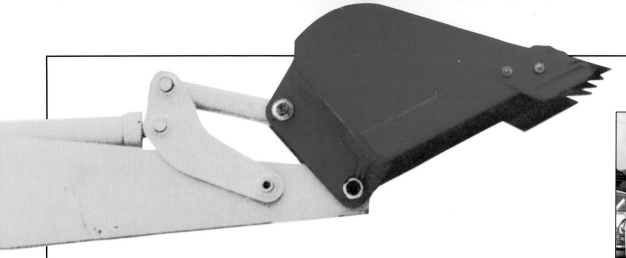

Mr Bamford in 1964 with his Rolls-Royce.
He visited the first operators in this way to
present their in-cab kettle.

This was all good clean fun to Mr JCB. He was fearless and had good reason to be. For during the last twelve months he had faced a huge crisis over the supply of Ford skid units, and survived.

Since the Major Loader in the early fifties JCB had been wedded to Ford. Yet all that was to change in as bizarre a fashion as one can possibly imagine. Ford changed production of tractor skids from Dagenham to Basildon. They also changed the product. Unable to handle both, supplies dried up and JCB, Ford's largest UK customer at the time, was starved.

Cooper soon found himself on his way to Detroit with Joe Bamford. The mission was simple - thump the table in the office of Henry Ford II and not leave without guarantees.

Alan Cooper: "We sat there just the three of us; myself and Joe and Henry Ford who didn't know what the hell was going on in England. They had kept it all from him. He turned to Mr Bamford and said 'don't you worry Joe, we'll get you the supplies you need'.

"Although we were Ford's biggest customer in England we were still a small company. We had a big wage bill and we were on our uppers. You just imagine it. There was no run-out, supplies just stopped."

Ford was in such a mess at Basildon that Cooper soon found himself out at Ford's plant in Brazil buying up whatever he could. He also went to Spain on the same crusade. Rocester was so desperate that Ford tractors arrived complete. They were disassembled, the skids rushed to the production line, and the other bits sent back to Brazil.

But there was worse to come.

JCB had become wary of single sourcing of major components and had earlier tested the BMC Nuffield agricultural skid unit. This was manufactured at the British Leyland plant in Bathgate, near Edinburgh.

Mr Bamford deduced that a safe future needed a new concept floating; that a skid unit is merely a power source which can be changed, rather than something central to the heart of the machine. And so JCB took its boldest gamble and switched to the Nuffield, an agricultural power unit which had to be uprated to withstand industrial use.

At Rocester on launch day, dealers were assembled in a wooden hut inside the huge new factory construction being built to house the new backhoe loader production line.

These Ford stalwarts were about to be shocked. Mr Bamford had instructed Alan Cooper to have a pit dug in the bare earth of what soon would be the new factory floor.

Cooper; "He wanted dealers to know that we believed so much in our products. We had invested everything in the new production facilities. Nothing was going to stop us, not Ford's problems, not anyone. This was our commitment, and he wanted to give them a lasting impression of our feelings."

With a lone trumpeter playing The Last Post, a Ford skid was lowered into the grave-like pit. Immediately afterwards, to the Reveille fanfare, the new Nuffield skid was revealed.

Cooper: "Oh we really had some fun that day. Ford were furious, so incensed that they threatened to sue us over the incident. They never did though."

Dealers faced a dilemma, having to choose which way to go. Some were flown to the States to see Ford's new backhoe loader, direct competition to JCB. On the one hand was Ford and the Ford backhoe, which all fitted in well with their other Ford business interests. On the other was JCB with the Nuffield power unit, which did not fit with the Ford business.

Mr Bamford with the first machine exported to the USA, a 4C leaving the factory in 1964. USA subsidiary JCB Inc was established at White Marsh near Baltimore, Maryland in 1970.

A complete JCB 3 chassis being lowered to a 57 bhp Fordson Major skid in 1962. The 3 was the first to have the JCB Hydraslide whereby the excavator could be positioned to suit the operator and the job in hand. It was still necessary to lock the kingpost assembly in place manually with a spanner.

Yet almost all dealers stuck with JCB, setting up separate companies to handle the franchise. There was now added benefit in JCB being able to deal with the entire warranty and full parts support on the Nuffield skid, instead of having to refer back to Ford. This put JCB one hundred per cent in control.

The factory had worked night and day to engineer the new engine into the complete backhoe loader line. The JCB 4, 3 , 4C, 3C, 2 and 2B all had to be re-engined and everybody connected to engineering departments who could wield a spanner was out there in the factory doing what they could to help.

Meanwhile as part of the distributor contracts, the JCB logo was to be used in every separate distributor company name. JCB was growing but now it had a way to appear even larger than life.

The Bathgate factory was to supply Rocester until a crippling strike in the winter of 1982. JCB, its biggest customer, was scheduled to take 5,500 of the 98 Series engine that year in a deal worth over £5m . With the Bathgate workers still out and ignoring warnings about losing the JCB business, Rocester's production lines faced run out in the week beginning 22nd February. JCB had no intention of running dry and on 12th February it was announced that a deal had been made for supply to switch to Perkins of Peterborough.

Gilbert Johnston, chief executive until August 1992 had experienced the Ford problems of 1966 just two years after he joined the company. When the British Leyland problems hit in 1982 JCB was better prepared, there had already been engineering work done on a variety of alternative engines, including Perkins.

Johnston: "In the late seventies we had developed our own axles which were produced at the new JCB Transmissions plant at Wrexham.

This was crucial as it meant we were no longer locked into any one tractor skid manufacturer. It was all pretty well thought out. When we told Bathgate we would have to switch if they didn't get back to work we were not bluffing. We had our options in place."

Today JCB sources components from engine suppliers such as Perkins, Cummins, Peugeot and Isuzu; also transmissions from JCB Transmissions and ZF.

The new BMC Nuffield skid unit of 1965 produced for JCB at the Bathgate factory following Ford's inability to maintain supplies despite an assurance by Henry Ford face to face with Joe Bamford.

A confidential pocket book was issued to salesmen in the mid sixties. The cover was leather bound to ensure a long life, and inside was useful engineering data on all JCB machines and the competition too. Mr Bamford's message on the first page is as true today as it ever was.
Book courtesy John Kilby, general manager, Scot JCB (Borders) Ltd.

Pictured outside the Rocester main entrance in 1964: Leroy Watson Jr, Mr Bamford and Anthony, Theo Fischer, President of JCB International, Dr Roger Voumard, director of JCB International, Harry Wilson, sales director JCB. Mrs Marjorie Bamford with Mrs Watson senior and Mrs Leroy Watson Jr.

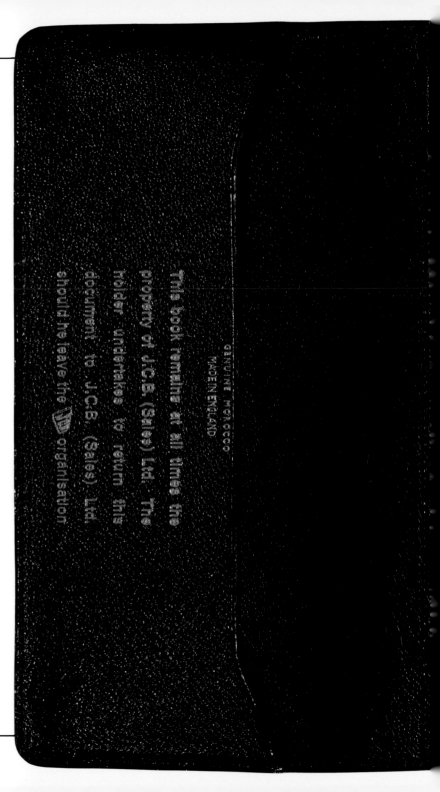

This book remains at all times the property of J.C.B. (Sales) Ltd. The holder undertakes to return this document to J.C.B. (Sales) Ltd. should he leave the organisation

GENUINE MOROCCO
MADE IN ENGLAND

A MESSAGE FROM

THE CHAIRMAN AND MANAGING DIRECTOR

Knowledge of your product is absolutely essential in today's competitive market.

Nothing destroys a client's confidence in a representative more than to hear his constant admission that he 'does not know'.

Nothing destroys a salesman's confidence in himself more than his failure to answer the client's questions about the products he is endeavouring to sell him.

(However an admission of lack of knowledge although inexcusable is far better than bluff. Remember "I don't know", "I'm not sure", I'll find out and let you know immediately". BE SURE YOU DO.) It is your only solution.

Knowledge of your products is perhaps the easiest of personal qualities to acquire, other people can help you acquire this knowledge. Never sit back thinking you know it all. Never be afraid to ask a question. Phone or write for information immediately.

Being in possession of the answers always inspires confidence and this easy to follow pocket reference book embracing facts and features of JB products, has been specially compiled for YOU.

Always carry this book with you.

Enjoying work

Amidst all the drama of the sixties, there was concentration on developing professional selling techniques.

When the plant hire industry became virtually the exclusive preserve of the JCB 3C in 1963 there was much to be done in building that dominance.

The sales force always had to be out in their territories, and had to have good reason to be at Rocester unless they had customers on factory visits. Salesmen were always encouraged to bring customers to the factory because Mr Bamford was convinced that seeing the factory behind the products and the demonstrations would build confidence.

Many were to find excitement in these heady days. One of them was Jim Harrison, who joined in November 1962 when the company was still only employing about 350 people, and the massive buildings expansion had not begun.

Jim: "I wouldn't call it impressive then, but there was something about it. When you walked in everybody seemed to be working and enjoying it, whereas the people where I had been working didn't."

Harrison, later to be appointed to several directorships in his career, took the job as northern area sales rep at less salary than his other job.

Harrison: "No-one, as far as I could see, had any great academic ability, but Mr Bamford could motivate people. He would listen to everyone and he was always challenging his senior people. He would listen to everyone, whether the ideas were good or not."

"I always remember you thought you had a thing all buttoned up and he would have the knack of finding the one flaw in your argument. Then he would come to the sales meetings and defend his machine come what may. I very quickly learned he was giving us sales arguments to bolster our morale."

The need for an excavator to suit the small builder was identified with the JCB 1 in June 1963. Powered by a 22hp air cooled diesel engine and very manoeuvrable, it proved that what customers thought they wanted, but actually needed, were poles apart. With limited sales it was criticised for being too small, although Mr Bamford was convinced it had enormous potential.

At the turn of the year came the JCB 2, a scaled down version of the 3. It was followed by the 2B, with detachable backhoe. Both versions, together with the 3, were given 3 cylinder Nuffield rather than Ford skid units and the 3C and 4C followed suit with four cylinder units.

To complete this year of change JCB also introduced a new range of dumpers in 15, 22.5 and 30 cwt sizes.

They were not to last long, as JCB concentrated on machines for volume markets.

Professionalism had to shine through at every demonstration, no matter what the task. Competitors could turn up with dirty machines and operators in greasy overalls. Not JCB.

Machines had to be washed clean whatever the job, and with a selection of buckets each labelled. Operators had to be in clean overalls. Staff had to arrive early, often erecting a tent to make tea for visitors.

Advertising was in colour with machines beautifully photographed

Mr Bamford with loud hailer in hand enjoying work as usual. He is explaining benefits of the JCB 3 to the first overseas distributors' conference in April 1962.

in unusual locations. When the competition copied with two page colour spreads, JCB would move up to six pages.

Jim Harrison: "We were a puny little outfit projecting ourselves bigger than we really were, and that's partly how the name became established."

In 1962 demonstrator Noel Hooper won £5 from Mr Bamford for this idea performed for the TV cameras. The 'up and under' has since been used in all JCB Dancing Digger shows.

Since the stunt with the JCB 4 and the Cadillac, the company saw the value of TV coverage. In December 1962 ABC Weekend transmitted the Sing Along programme, recorded earlier at Lakeside Works and featuring amongst others singer Dennis Lotis and Mrs Mills at the piano. Here a cameraman focuses on a JCB 3 logo. JCB has featured in many productions through the years from drama to the recent and phenomenally popular 'You Bet' series.

Mr Bamford is carried shoulder high by Bill Hirst and John Wheeldon in January 1964 at the surprise announcement of a quarter million pound service award payout. Many employees took home pay packets with £300 to £500 inside. The bumper payout was made possible by the 60% trading increase of 1963.

JCB promotional items today cover everything from tea mugs, T shirts and hundreds of different designs for ties. Yet the ideas go back a long way. Yellow caps for operators were available in 1962 at 7s 6d. Many thousands of diecast scale models have been produced over the years like this modern 3CX. The first model known was a JCB 3 sold in Woolworth stores and toyshops in 1963 for 3 shillings.

The demonstration team in 1965 with the JCB 7, the company's first 360 degree tracked excavator. It was manufactured under licence from Warner Swasey. The superstructure and hydraulics were Warner Swasey's Hopto design whilst JCB made the undercarriage and the excavator assembly.
Left to right: Walter Cope, Charlie Heaton, Noel Hooper in the cab, Reg Williams, Maurice Weston, John Wheeldon, Ken Harrison, and Gerry Highfield in the bucket.

The launch of the JCB 7 in October 1964 with management making up the band whilst real bandsmen played behind the scenes. Left to right top row: Alec Kelly, John Honey, John Wheeldon, Jim Harrison; bottom row Jennie Starkey, Captain Mike Sutton, Alan Cooper, Gilbert Johnston, Noel Hooper, Harry Wilson, Mike Whyles.

New directions

A new direction was taken in 1964 when the culmination of several years development produced the JCB 7 - the company's first 360 degree crawler excavator, based on the American Hopto design and Ford powered. The range was rapidly expanded by the introduction of three more models in 1966 - the JCB 6, 6C and 7B.

The 6 and 6C had tumbler tracks which were not efficient. The 7B was the first JCB tracked excavator with the now familiar tooth and sprocket drive design.

There was heavy concentration on promotion, with advertising designed to dominate the construction media. The JCB logo was becoming a symbol for construction machines in the public's eye.

By now JCB was renowned not only for high quality and innovative engineering, but also for its marketing flair. In 1967 this latter aspect was to furnish a real eye-opener with the launch of the JCB 3D, preceded by revised Mark II versions of the 3C and 4C with restyled cabs.

JCB launched the larger, heavier 3D with theatrical flair, raising a full sized model from a swimming pool and leaving it suspended mid-air.

Many ideas are continually tested as prototypes without ever going into production. Here is one such, a 6C of 1968 with a crane jib working on construction at the factory.

A futuristic round cab idea of 1965, which was abandoned.

In 1968, led by Anthony Bamford, JCB acquired Chaseside Engineering of Blackburn, the pioneers of wheeled loading shovels in Britain and with a wealth of experience in a specialised market. JCB had produced a prototype during the mid 1960's, but never put it into production. Chaseside had a range of seven machines at take-over, with 15 per cent of the British market.

The face of JCB was changing again. By 1968 extensive factory re-development was under way. A new assembly hall was already in use, having been completed at a cost of £3 million and the research and service division sections were being erected. Landscaping would create a factory blending harmoniously with the rural Staffordshire countryside.

The factory had begun with 4,560 sq ft in 1950, and by 1970 had reached 622,900 sq ft. Yet this tremendous expansion was still little more than half what the Rocester factory was to become in the years ahead.

The close of an eventful decade for JCB included further revisions to the crawler excavator range, the opening of an office for JCB Canada in Toronto and launch of the JCB 700.

Work began on the service and research areas in March 1968. The first phase, occupation of the computer suite, was May 1969, and final stage occupation May 1970.

In 1969 more than 50 per cent of production was for export and Mr Bamford's outstanding record of achievement was acknowledged with his award of a CBE for services to exports.

And so the 1970s arrived with introduction of the larger engined JCB 2D and JCB 1250 loading shovel. The pace was not to slacken as 1971 rolled in and JCB launched its biggest crawler excavator yet - the 8C - soon replaced with the 8D. A JCB 902 loading shovel replaced the 900, and the 2D, 6C and 7C were discontinued.

In 1970 JCB entered the finance business, with the establishment of JCB Credit , which therefore celebrates its Silver Jubilee in 1995. JCB Credit is UK market leader in providing finance for JCB and other non-competitive equipment. It employs 55 people in the restored Rocester Mill by the side of the River Churnet, and is owned by The Lombard and Ulster Bank and JCB. Lombard and Ulster is the majority shareholder.

It was the idea of Gilbert Johnston and is remarkable because it is a joint venture finance house dedicated to the JCB product and dealer network, but it does not tie up the cash which JCB prefers to invest back into manufacturing.

Gilbert Johnston believes that this joint venture is a very interesting stake in manufacturer-led credit. "It is one hundred per cent committed to our business, but it doesn't tie up our cash. Therefore it is a very good formula that has worked very well for all parties."

On 17 December 1970 an American distribution centre was opened at Baltimore and JCB took a bold step into another new market.

Gilbert Johnston

JCB France was established in 1972 as the first wholly owned subsidiary. It was a landmark in Rocester taking control of overseas distribution and was used virtually as a blueprint for the future. Germany, Holland, the USA, Italy and Spain were to follow this lead.

For legal reasons Anthony Bamford and Gilbert Johnston had only four months to do it all. They began at the end of October 1971 and the structure was in place by the following February; premises, dealers, the lot.

Johnston: "We worked solidly for those four months but we achieved it, which was remarkable."

Sales for the year exceeded all previous records to establish JCB as market leader in France.

The operation began with four employees. Patrick Massardy was the first managing director, Pierre Leboucher was service director. Françoise Rausch looked after the administration and Pierre Mouries was in charge of promotion and marketing.

The distribution was immediately organised with former JCB agents, led by the largest one, Lyomat, a JCB dealer since 1960. Pierre Leboucher was later appointed managing director and in 1983 became one of the few Frenchmen ever to be awarded the OBE for services to British exports.

Today he is European director in charge of strategies and logistics in JCB Europe. He looks after France, Italy, Germany and JCB's latest subsidiary company in Spain, JCB Maquinaria. Françoise Rausch is now managing director of JCB France.

Chaseside loading shovels were in full production at Rocester by 1969. Initially these had the Chaseside rigid chassis design, but soon JCB was to introduce its own centre pivot articulating machines with the engine mounted on the rear module.

The new JCB 110 was seen by Mr Bamford as "one of the most significant JCB achievements in the past 15 years", and hailed by the specialist press. It was the world's first hydrostatic crawler loader and won the Design Council Award. Although revolutionary in all respects it was later abandoned when the crawler loader market went into sharp decline.

Meanwhile, after four years development JCB was also ready to launch its first "all JCB" loading shovels.

The new 413 and 418 replaced existing Chaseside models and the JCB 400 Series was launched in 1971.

For 1973 the main project was to launch a new range of crawler excavators with dual hydraulics and a high percentage of parts interchangeability.

The JCB 806 and 807 had complete new designs and were joined in 1975 by the larger 808. As now, JCB has always believed in updating models or ranges as required to meet demand.

In 1975 JCB 423 and 428 articulated wheeled loaders were introduced as larger additions to that range. The JCB 112 joined the 110 in an attempt to boost the crawler loader range.

The company had grown very quickly, and bore little resemblance to its former self. It was a force to be reckoned with.

Now came a time for personal decision; Mr Bamford had discussed with Anthony the possibility of retiring. When the time came Mr JCB was in his 60th year. Anthony was just thirty, and there was only a few months difference in age from when his father had started the business back in 1945.

The year 1975 was drawing to a close.

At Lakeside Works, Rocester, senior executives settled into the comfortable 230 seat presentation theatre. They were more used to standing out front as presenters than to sitting back as an audience. They reasoned a pep talk from the founder Mr JCB would surely follow soon.

Not so. It was Anthony who walked from behind the curtains onto the stage.

"Gentlemen, as I speak to you my father is on his way to Europe. He has retired. I am your new Chairman."

And so ended the first chapter in the history of JCB.

The innovative centre pivot steer JCB 413
of 1972 showing the cab and loader on the
front module and the engine in the rear
module.
The pivot was constructed from a vertically
mounted cross roll slew ring as used on
JCB hydraulic excavators. This was one of
Mr JCB's innovative design contributions.

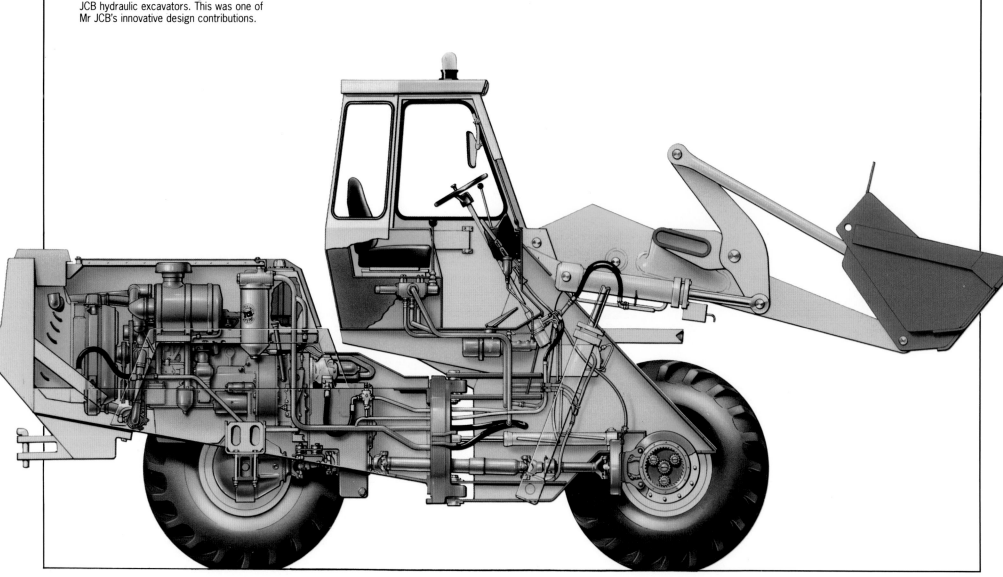

This simple message stunned a workforce which had not lived a day without the 'old man' there in person, by telephone or by telex. Although a well-kept secret Mr Bamford had discussed retirement in the preceding months with Anthony before the final decision was made. His retirement actually took place in November 1975 but the official announcement was saved until December 31.

Jamais Content B

Never content

66 The 'old man' of the team has decided to retire.

At nearly 60 years of age it is time for me to give some of the younger management the opportunity to show its strengths.

JCB is still a young and virile company that knows its path for the future and unlike most others it has all the determination to succeed.

What our company has achieved in the past is simply history. What is achieved next year and onwards will determine your security and personal prosperity.

Anthony faces the tough job of moving JCB forward through the next decades and in to a new century. This is a demanding task but he has been well trained for it and is supported by a very strong team from works staff to management. There cannot be any limit to the successes.

JCB is established now as one of the major forces in British and European industry, thanks to your efforts. The tragedy is that other companies have never tried as hard for Great Britain.

Thank you for what you have done to earn our company such an enviable reputation.

A happy and prosperous New Year to you and your family 99

J. C. Bamford CBE
Founder   December 31, 1975

CHAPTER TWO

Interesting pointers along the way

JCB makes legal history

During 1966 proposals had been made by JCB to merge its business with the agricultural business carried on by Bamfords Ltd, the company from which Mr JCB had broken away to start his own business in 1945. The merger proposals were not welcomed by Mr JCB's cousins, the directors of Bamfords Ltd.

Early in November 1967, JCB made a take-over bid, offering 12/- for each Bamfords share; an offer that was subsequently increased to 15/- per share. However, on 20 November 1967, the directors of Bamfords Ltd issued 500,000 new shares in the company to Frederick Burgess Ltd at the shares' par value of 4/-, despite the offer on the table from JCB of 12/- per share. FHB Ltd was a principal distributor of Bamfords Ltd products, and the directors of Bamfords Ltd said they considered it would be advantageous for such an important distributor to have a direct stake in Bamfords Ltd.

However, the following day, November 21, Anthony Bamford, who was a shareholder in Bamfords Ltd, with his uncle Rupert Bamford, who had resigned the day before as a director of Bamfords Ltd, issued a writ against the remaining directors, Henry Bamford, Richard Bamford and John Bamford, as well as Frederick Burgess Ltd and Bamfords Ltd itself, for a declaration that the issue of the 500,000 shares was invalid and of no effect, on the grounds that the directors had issued shares in bad faith and not in the bona fide interests of the company and the other shareholders, but merely as a tactical move to block the take-over bid by JCB.

Tim Leadbeater, now group commercial director, was at the time an articled clerk with a local firm of solicitors and it was he who had to serve writs on the Bamfords Ltd directors.

He remembers this included waiting in the shadows outside John Bamford's house one evening to serve a writ as he returned home from the cinema.

The case first came to court in March 1968, and finally in the Court of Appeal the following year. Quintin Hogg QC, now Lord Hailsham, was one of the barristers who appeared for the JCB side. Ultimately, whether or not the 500,000 shares were properly issued or not did not affect the outcome of the take-over bid, but even today, law students and judges alike know Bamford v Bamford as the legal authority and precedent that even if directors have acted in bad faith and from an improper motive, any impropriety on their part can be subsequently validated by the shareholders in a general meeting. No-one will ever know what might have been if the take-over bid had succeeded, as although 80% of the individual shareholders wanted to accept the JCB offer, the holders of more than 51% of the shares by value continued to block the take-over.

Bamfords Ltd ultimately went into liquidation in 1980. Whether if JCB had taken over it would have been saved from liquidation can only be speculation, as well as what might have been the consequences for JCB itself if its focus had been diverted from its core business, for at the time of the take-over bid Bamfords Ltd was in fact already making losses.

The connection with Bamfords Ltd did not however end with the failure of the take-over bid and the end of the court proceedings. Rupert Bamford until his retirement worked for International Transmissions Ltd both in Ireland and at Wrexham. Mr JCB's younger brother, DC 'Tim' Bamford, who had backed the JCB take-over bid, subsequently took over the ownership and running of Iracroft, which had itself been rescued by JCB from the Receiver. Iracroft to this day remains a key supplier of hydraulic pipework to JCB.

After the liquidation in 1980, the old business of Bamfords Ltd was sold by the liquidators to a new company called Bamfords International, owned by a Mr Mohamed Zabadne. In February 1989, the old Bamfords Ltd factory was acquired from Mr Zabadne. The factory is currently occupied by JCB Special Products Ltd and JCB-

A hard hitting leaflet put out by JCB in 1967 during the takeover battle.

SCM, but when JCB Special Products Ltd moves to its new custom-built factory in Cheadle in the summer of 1995, JCB-SCM will take over occupation of the whole factory. The Bamford business connection with Uttoxeter goes back to the establishment of a blacksmith's shop in 1812.

The directors of Bamfords, Ltd. have rejected the 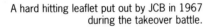 proposals, which would have resulted in greater security and higher wages for Bamfords' employees, plus greater prosperity for the town of Uttoxeter

The JCB proposals to the Board of Bamfords Limited are:

£750,000 of new cash capital – enough to halve the company's overdraft and reduce interest payments by about £70,000 per year.

Sub contract work to the value of £1M annually – this would earn the company £100,000 per year in extra profits.

Two entirely new products to be marketed through Bamfords' dealer network and produced with the backing of the highly successful JCB design and development team.

Service contracts for Bamfords' directors and senior executives – a security they do not now have – plus the benefits of increased production resulting in higher wages for all employees.

JCB Rocester Uttoxeter Staffs

SPECIAL

WEALTH   TUESDAY, OCTOBER 14, 1958   PRICE 2½d.

rs down tools

FLIGHTS
e crisis

Johannesburg, Singapore, Lagos, Montreal, and to New York were involved.

About 300 men downed tools when union officials told them five men had been sacked.

A union spokesman said : "This is a victimisation. The five dismissed men were on major checks of aircraft. The decision to stop work immediately was taken at a mass meeting."

He added that pickets would remain on guard through the night and inform employees arriving for the first day shift at 6.30 a.m. He estimated that by later today 4,000 men would be on strike.

The slow-up at London Airport was organised by shop stewards as a protest against the "inadequacy" of a pay increase of 5s. 6d. to 7s. 4d. week.

The offer is still under consideration, and national officers of the unions concerned have warned the shop stewards their action is unconstitutional.

m kidnapped

Mr JCB buys 10 scooters for JCB 1

By JOHN LEY

WEALTHY manufacturer Joseph Cyril Bamford dreamed of the day when he could own a car with the registration number JCB 1—his own initials.

For ten years he tried unsuccessfully to satisfy his "pet whim." He wrote letter after letter to the motor licensing authorities, but they refused to reserve his special number.

But now he has achieved his ambition by buying ten motor scooters at a cost of £2,000.

Forty-two-year-old Mr. Bamford made one vital condition when he placed the order with a surprised Blackburn scooter dealer—that the registration numbers of the scooters should be JCB 1 to 10, the current issue by the borough of Blackburn.

Transfer

The scooter-dealer succeeded where Mr. Bamford failed. When the first scooter arrived a quick transfer was arranged, and now JCB 1 is the registration number of Mr. Bamford's new 135 m.p.h. five-litre Continental Bentley.

Britain's amazing trade swing in a year

By L. D. WILLIAMS

FOR the first time in a century Britain has wiped out the gap in "visible" trade.

We sold £137,000,000 worth more goods abroad than we bought overseas during the first six months of this year.

Visible trade is the exchange of actual goods . . . the cars, machinery, and textiles, we ship OUT, and the food and materials that are brought IN.

"Invisible" exports are the money our ships earn in transporting goods, oil receipts, investments abroad, and banking receipts.

The switch

Every year since 1850 the money earned by invisible exports has had to be set against deficits on visible trade. But this year visible trade stood on its own feet.

From January to June we imported £1,816,000,000 worth of goods. But we sold £1,753,000,000 abroad. It is a remarkable switch.

Only six previously—from July to December 1957—there was a £31,000,000 deficit in visible trade, and back in 1955 the gap was as much as £350,000,000.

The reason for the switch? The fall in payments for imports mainly because the prices of goods we bought abroad fell, The

LATEST

Mr Bamford bought ten motor scooters in 1958 with the proviso they must have registration plates from JCB 1 to JCB 10. The plates are transferred to new vehicles through the years and the company still acquires more whenever possible.

Since the days at Crakemarsh stables Mr Bamford had dreamed of owning a car with the registration number JCB 1. He tried unsuccessfully to satisfy this whim for years, writing letters to the motor licensing authorities. But they refused to reserve a special number.

Then in October 1958 he achieved his ambition by buying ten motor scooters for £2,000. He made one vital condition when he placed the order with a scooter dealer in Blackburn. The registration numbers of the scooters should be JCB 1 to 10, the current issue by the borough of Blackburn.

The scooter dealer succeeded where Joe had failed. When the first scooter arrived JCB 1 was transferred to his new red and white Bentley Continental. JCB 2 was reserved at the time for Marjorie Bamford's new car.

Mr Bamford sold all the scooters to employees on a no-deposit no-interest easy-payment basis. Everyone who bought had to sign an agreement to transfer the scooters registration numbers if the company should ever need them. It did.

Since then, the company has bought many more registration plates with the JCB initials before the letters. There are now 82 registration plates where the JCB initials come first.

JCB 1 is the lowest number and JCB 968 is the highest so far.

The company owns JCB 1 to JCB 14; 15 and 16 are missing, but the company owns 17 to 20.

There are still a few numbers around not owned by the company, with current owners unwilling to sell for sentimental reasons.

"We won't pay silly money" says assistant company secretary Les Mitchell, official keeper of registration plates.

Some registration numbers can never be purchased, lost for ever when vehicles were scrapped in the sixties and seventies without being transferred to the computer records at DVLC Swansea. With the source drying up, the company is able to buy only perhaps one plate a year now.

Now, Les Mitchell has turned to DVLC auctions, and has been able in this way to acquire some plates where the number precedes the initials. In this way the company now has 1 JCB, through to 6 JCB.

The JCB number plates are all in use and are on directors' cars, sales and service engineers' cars, as well as vans and trucks. And JCB's company cars have been white ever since Mr Bamford read research reports suggesting white as the safest colour to have on the road.

Before this however the first cars for the sales representatives, John Wheeldon and Ken Cadwallader, were two Ford Anglias painted red and yellow with a JCB logo bolted to the boot lid to project JCB's image. John Skeldon, the first sales director, had one as well on his Ford Zephyr.

The company's first customer limousine was a huge 1960 left-hand-drive Cadillac Fleetwood, which had seven seats to match the first aircraft, the de Havilland Dove. It collected customers when the Dove landed at Tatenhill Airfield, near Burton on Trent. Denis Bettany of the Rocester family and later garage manager, was the company's first uniformed chauffeur with the Cadillac.

JCB was asked to loan a Rolls-Royce as back-up vehicle for a Royal visit in 1977 to Derby. When the Buckingham Palace car broke down Her Majesty The Queen was saved embarrassment. The JCB car was following. Glad to be of help Ma'am.

The company's first customer limousine was this huge Cadillac Fleetwood pictured on 2nd May 1961 at Birmingham Airport with Exporter, JCB's first de Havilland Dove. The Cadillac was chosen because seating capacity matched that of the aircraft so customers could be ferried easily to the factory.

HOW TO SELL A DIGGER AT 30,000 FEET

JCB Aviation operates one fixed wing aircraft and one helicopter. But whenever a new aircraft is delivered it allows the opportunity for an unusual photograph to be taken with new and old side by side. This picture shows aircraft in JCB livery outside the JCB Aviation hangar at the East Midlands Airport.

A fun cartoon window sticker occasionally seen on a briefcase or two at Rocester depicts a yellow backhoe loader with wings. The 'flying digger' is exactly that. The owner of the briefcase will almost certainly be a JCB company pilot.

The company's own aircraft have played a significant role in sales activities since the sixties. JCB Aviation is older than many airlines.

In many multi-nationals 'executive jet' means champagne exclusivity. Ultimate status beyond even the key to the executive washroom. Not so at JCB.

Here 'customer jet' would better describe the role. JCB Aviation is a department staffed with its own flight planning office at Rocester, two full time pilots for the British Aerospace 1000 Series, two full time helicopter pilots for the Agusta 109 Mk2, and two full time ground staff engineers based at a private hanger at East Midlands Airport.

Successive aircraft are each called 'Exporter'. The current 1000 Series, delivered new for 1994, is 'Exporter 10' and is well known to air traffic controllers throughout Europe under its call sign JCB One. The main airports visited regularly include Cologne, Paris, Milan, Maastricht, and Madrid.

Mr Bamford taking delivery of the company's first HS 125 executive jet in May 1970. This aircraft was painted yellow with a red horizontal strip and the unusual colour scheme gave rise to the nickname 'the bleeding banana'.

Whilst even personalised registration signs must remain with each aircraft throughout its flying life the identification call sign for JCB pilots remain whatever the aircraft. So 'JCB One' is known daily to air traffic controllers throughout Europe.

Mr Bamford gained his aviator's certificate in 1948 and this doubtless led to his appreciation of the value of aircraft for export sales missions.

In Europe, the schedules for both the fixed wing and the helicopter are always full. It is a rare day which does not find the fixed wing aircraft operating between several European cities, collecting and returning customers on factory visits. Similarly the helicopter, call sign JCB Three, operates throughout the UK.

Aircraft make it possible for a customer to be picked up locally in the morning, spend as much time as possible during the day at the factory on a visit tailored specifically to his main interest, and then to be returned home again by evening.

Time Saving

The helicopter can land on its own helipad amidst landscaping and lakes to the east of the Rocester factory complex.

So here is the true rationale; time saving and efficiency aimed at the customer.

JCB came to this conclusion early in its development. Another consideration at the time was that the Rocester factory was in a rural area and not on the map for heavy industry.

Now, with growing congestion in traditional commercial areas, Rocester is easy to get to and its rural location is an ideal backdrop to worldwide activities.

Mr Bamford himself had trained as a pilot, and obtained his aviator's certificate (the pilot's licence of its day) from The Royal Aero Club in Piccadilly on 8th June 1948, two week's before his 32nd birthday. A keen private pilot he bought an Army surplus Auster in 1949. Another Auster followed and then a Miles Messenger.

He was not starry-eyed about the glamour of flying but saw the possibilities of owning a company aircraft for its true worth.

The first aircraft was a twin-engined de Havilland Dove. Enid Lee, now secretary to engineering and research director Bob Pendlebury was 19 when she won £6 in a works competition to name the new aircraft.

Enid put in a very late entry and suggested 'Explorer' unaware a decision had already been taken to call it 'Exporter'. Enid was judged the winner and invited to join a business trip to Hull.

The first company pilot was Captain Mike Sutton, a former de Havilland company test pilot. The Dove saw service throughout the UK and Europe doing much the same job as the current aircraft.

It was followed by a last of the line Series 8 Dove with a special executive interior. The first aircraft is still owned by the company today. When it was withdrawn from service it was mothballed. With its right wing removed and stored in a packing crate, the red and white machine rests above an office unit in the Research Department.

JCB pilots regard themselves as ambassadors of the company and keep themselves up to date with product information in order to be able to hold persuasive conversations with customers.

Captain Phil Zarraga ready for another day's business in the skies of Europe.
JCB Aviation was formed in 1961 with the delivery of the company's first aircraft G-ARJB and it is therefore older than many scheduled airlines.

Captain Phil Zarraga, a former Shackleton and Nimrod pilot does most of the flying on the fixed wing with Captain David Patterson. Captain Ivor Johnstone MBE and Captain Rob Stubbs fly the helicopter.

Using Fun To Sell

JCB has always been keenly aware that a slice of action will draw a crowd.

This simple observation has been put into practice in many ways to draw attention to the product. It has led to a dual role for the factory demonstration team. On the one hand, the team demonstrates seriously to customers. On the other it becomes the JCB Dancing Diggers formation team.

About 1962 Mr Bamford called for ideas that would attract the interest of a TV producer. Company demonstrator Noel Hooper thought of raising a backhoe loader by placing the back bucket flat against the ground and pressing down. Instead of digging, this technique will lift the entire chassis clear of the ground. The leading edge of the front bucket pivots with the ground and maintains vertical stability. It looks impressive and demonstrates hydraulic power.

Noel lifted the machine up and the late Harry Moult, chauffeur at the time, drove the company's Cadillac underneath. This stunt, now called the up and under, appeared on television and Joe Bamford paid Noel Hooper £5 for coming up with it.

One of the early sixties demonstrators was Reg Williams, and he was immediately impressed with Noel's idea. He felt there was something worth developing. When Reg was appointed foreman in 1965 – a position he held for 21 years until 1986 – demonstrations were held on the car park next to the cheese factory. The first routine was the JCB Salute, done with two backhoe loaders leaning out in a fan shape.

One of Noel Hooper's other great ideas was laying a backhoe loader down on its side. By folding up the excavator arm quickly and pressing against the ground it is possible to right the entire machine without harm.

The seeds were sown. By the end of the sixties the demonstration team had its own workshop, demonstration yard, and best of all in 1968 the company bought part of the old Derby Road airfield at Ashbourne. Reg Williams saw the opportunity to develop entire routines and he set about building props such as see-saws for loading shovels.

Reg Williams: "We realised with two of any type of machine we could run a show. We even built table top scale models and worked out whole routines. Then we latched onto themes such as bullfights and 'High Noon' shoot outs, that's how it all started".

Having fun with JCB 3Cs at a 1969 London street parade.

The first appearance of the JCB Circus, now called the Dancing Diggers, was at Ashbourne demonstration ground in 1970 to celebrate Anthony Bamford's 25th birthday. Chaseside loading shovels, then new in production at JCB, were included in the line up. The original idea was inspired by the RAF Red Arrows, but as the demonstration team dressed in white overalls the formation was first called the White Arrows, later the JCB Circus.

Today the JCB Dancing Diggers practice complex manoeuvres which show to best advantage many of the company's products. Besides the original up and under, the figure of eight, the star and the wheel are just some of the routines which are rehearsed to perfection.

The team has now performed for countless thousands of spectators in many countries. It has performed before Heads of State, members of the Royal Family, and has featured in numerous television appearances.

The JCB Dancing Diggers demonstrate product strength and corporate ingenuity, and have become a firm favourite at shows through the years.

A zany vehicle built in the eighties made no pretence at being anything other than a joke. Fun was the message, pure and simple. It was the JCB GT.

This unique machine was launched to the Press at Donington Race Circuit on the morning of August 1st 1988.

Australian motorcycle police showed more than passing interest in the JCB GT in Adelaide when David Whiston pulled in for petrol at a roadside filling station. November 1990.

It didn't make the charts, but USA salesman Lenny Green's 1988 Country 'n Western single made history, and money for the National Society for Prevention of Cruelty to Children.

The JCB Dancing Diggers is a co-ordinated routine of mechanical muscle. After more than 30 years this 'up and under' routine is still an excellent way to demonstrate hydraulic power. The action here dates from the demonstration yard in 1978.

COME AND SEE THE **JCB** CIRCUS
SPRING SHOW 80
6-10 MAY SHOWS TWICE DAILY
RDS BALLSBRIDGE

The JCB GT story is an interesting one for those fascinated by the principle of taking a seemingly crazy idea and turning it to advantage.

The JCB GT was built to look exactly like a normal JCB backhoe loader. But close inspection revealed otherwise. The body was moulded in glassfibre and fooled the eye because fine detail line weld seams on excavator assemblies were faithfully reproduced.

Under the skin instead of a Perkins diesel, there was a V8 Chevrolet 7440cc engine, converted for quarter mile dash dragster racing. It had a belt-driven 871 supercharger. Drive was torque converter to a GM Turbo 400 three-speed gearbox, which was very heavily modified to cope.

This was great fun to watch, but fearsome to drive.

The idea for the machine came from Anthony Bamford in 1985 when Irish comedian Frank Carson was regularly using a joke as part of his stage routine. The joke was about Irish labourers wanting a JCB GT for Christmas.

Little did Carson realise at the time that three years later he would be appearing before the national Press and TV cameras to launch the real JCB GT not with Champagne, but a bottle of Guinness.

It was the fastest JCB in the world, capable of 100 mph on four wheels in a straight line.

The JCB GT ran at major events from 1988 to 1990. Without doubt it gave many thousands of people a lot of amusement. It entertained at major motor racing events including the British Formula One Grand Prix in July 1990. It was dismantled, crated and shipped to Australia, and re-assembled locally for the Australian Formula One Grand Prix in Adelaide, in the November.

Other fun ideas over the years have included forays into the world of music, such as JCB and Me, issued as a single by American JCB salesman and Country and Western artist Lenny Green. The cover of the 45 rpm record showed Lenny Green with a North American build JCB in Monument Valley.

There is even the official JCB Fanfare, composed in 1984 by the bandmaster of the Band of The Royal Marines. On a visit to the Rocester factory it was recorded live by the band on stage in the JCB theatre. The JCB Fanfare is now used at the end of every performance by the JCB Dancing Diggers, wherever they are in the world.

The 100 mph JCB GT wheelie machine attracted the attention of Autocar & Motor in this unusual 1988 road test.

A rare collectors item is the first single, issued as a 45 rpm record in 1965. The 'JCB March' was recorded by the Regimental Band of the 1st Battalion, The King's Shropshire Light Infantry. The sleeve showed a 1950 photo of the cheese factory.

This 110B was photographed in South America in 1978 for a worldwide corporate advertising campaign which made the claim 'No Place For Second Best'.

CHAPTER THREE

Taking the company to new heights

Anthony Bamford in 1980 launching an advertising campaign drawing attention to the value-for-money benefits of buying the new JCB 3CX.

The Big Change

1976 to 1995

Although he took over in November 1975, public announcement of Anthony's appointment was not made until January 1, 1976. At 30 years of age he had become managing director of the company now with a turnover of £43 million. Factory production area covered a million square feet and output was rising.

Now, in 1995, turnover is approaching £700 m for the group and factory production is still rising. But the Rocester site has reached its limit with 1.2 m sq ft, and this was one of the factors behind the opening of new plants at Cheadle, Uttoxeter and Rugeley. This is inevitably the only way that volume can continue to increase. These are the dynamics of the business that JCB has pursued so single mindedly; the dynamics of change.

But back in the seventies Rocester was the sole manufacturing unit. There was still space to build new bays to accommodate new lines. More telescopic handlers, loading shovels and tracked excavators were being built.

The last crawler loader model, the JCB 114, was introduced during 1976 but with the market falling worldwide, these highly innovative machines were to have a short commercial life. Years later, when Caterpillar brought out a hydrostatic crawler the Rocester factory sent a little scale model of the JCB crawler to CAT with a note simply saying:
"Congratulations. Imitation is the highest form of flattery." As a manufacturer committed to volume production JCB had dropped its innovative crawler loader without shedding a tear.

Also that year, the 806B and 807B revised tracked excavators were launched.

The JCB 520 Telescopic Handler came in October 1977 to a blaze of publicity. This was JCB's answer in Europe to those much larger forward reach machines operating in North America. It was the result of a free thinking 'commando squad' whose brief was to break with convention. It was quickly learned that the concept needed to be four wheel drive, and in this later format was soon the company's second highest volume product, behind the backhoe loader.

Indeed the direct descendant of those early machines, the JCB Loadall range, is the company's second highest volume product today.

1978 through into 1979 was a time for decision making which, had it been wrong, could have had unthinkable implications. Here, with turnover a record £120 million and the 3C Mk 111 backhoe loader outselling all other competition put together, Anthony Bamford and the Executive board decided to kill off this golden goose and replace with a completely new design. This was the one product range which just had to be right, for it carried both the future of the company with it, and the past. A taste of what was to come had been provided by the

This artist's impression of the factory frontage is astonishingly close to the reality of today. Yet this vision of the future was conceived for Mr Joe Bamford when the factory was still little more than an old cheese factory and corrugated tin sheds. It was drawn in 1964, twenty five years before HRH The Princess Royal opened the JCB showroom and office complex on 26 June 1989.

inclusion of the new JCB Powertrain, including the JCB Max-Trac axle and the JCB Syncro Shuttle transmission during 1979 in both the JCB 3C III and JCB 3D models. This was the forerunner of the modular construction which was to follow in Project 200, the internal code name for the new 3CX.

In the 19 years from October 1961 when the first JCB 3 was produced until production of the JCB 3C III ceased during October 1980, nearly 72,000 backhoe loaders based on the ubiquitous JCB integral chassis design were sold. Nearly half were exported.

Project 200 is now still believed to be the most painstaking and intensive research and development programme carried out by any one company in the industry for a single product line. Derek Prime, the man who had originally conceived the 3C design back in the early sixties and who later became managing director of JCB Research following the death of development director Alec Kelly, took direct control of the design team working exclusively on Project 200.

Whilst Derek guided the design team, another senior director, Derek Danson, oversaw the production team. Danson had worked his way up through the company from buyer to head buyer, then through to managing director of JCB Service where he

This artist's impression from the early seventies is almost identical to today. Like the 1964 impression it has a strong vision of how a factory can be a showpiece; how dreams can become reality.

developed the parts and merchandising business, an essential mainstay to the growth of JCB.

Danson's ability to tackle difficult tasks made him right for the job of running the factory during this crucial period with all the complex changes needed to the assembly line in particular. Derek Danson died in May 1984. Gilbert Johnston remembers him as very determined: "Derek was absolutely uncompromising, come hell or high water he would get a job done."

More than 2,000 improvements had been incorporated in the 3C lineage by refinement and improvement over the years. It was time for a complete rethink and the most thorough investigation into contemporary backhoe loader design so far conducted was under way.

As part of the programme JCB invested £6 million in the new JCB Transmissions plant at Wrexham specifically to build Max-Trac axles.

Over £24 million was pumped into the new 3CX development programme, including new production technology to boost production levels by some 60 per cent and raise quality and reliability levels.

Part of an early eighties advertising campaign for the 3CX Sitemaster, promoting versatility.

To do all this in 1980 was a brave step for JCB, right in the middle of the industry's most severe recession ever. With the launch of the 3CX Sitemaster concept in 1981, JCB had hit on another winner. It resulted from analysis of customer uses and demand for attachments.

Also, the 1,000th Loadall was produced that year.

The JCB 410, first in a new range of loading shovels, had been launched in 1981 and was now joined by the larger 420 and 430.

By 1983 JCB had built its 10,000th 3CX backhoe loader - also the 100,000th machine to be made by JCB.

1984 became another record year. Turnover topped £150 million, exports exceeded 65 per cent of production, Loadall production reached 1,000 units a year.

JCB had come through the darker days of the seventies when ripples from the Heath Government's pay policy had reached Rocester, and encouraged those workers at the British Leyland engine factory at Bathgate to risk losing JCB.

The JCB 520 Telescopic Handler of 1977 was in a class of its own. But unlike the crawler loader and its shrinking market, the 520 TH was out to carve a new clientele interested in moving materials around site quickly and efficiently in an age of rising materials prices. It was the first small wheeled machine which could reach forward across obstructions.

There had been vigorous recovery from the recession of the early eighties and now, with record turnover being announced to workforce meetings by Gilbert Johnston with each passing year, JCB saw yet again the stage was set for change.

The sales teams were achieving higher market shares in the reputedly mature backhoe loader market. The task set was to achieve the same level of success with the other product ranges. Only the Loadalls had achieved true volume recognition. Anthony Bamford was looking for new product champions to challenge the production dominance of the backhoe loader cash cow. Only the JCB Loadall was making a significant challenge and he wanted to see more of this coming through.

It all had to change. It did.

The original 1977 JCB Materials Handling team under Jim Harrison (centre, grey suit) set out to break with convention and they did, forcing an unsuspecting market to take forward reach seriously. By 1978 the 100th machine had been built. Today JCB Loadalls are the company's second biggest volume product, beaten only by backhoe loader production. The 25,000th Loadall rolled off the Rocester production line on 7 March 1995.

Excellent seventies photography such as here, a backhoe loader pictured in New York, pursued a theme developed in the sixties. When the Financial Times first used colour printing, JCB was one of the first advertisers and these photographs were used.

Many of the techniques now familiar in consumer advertising were being utilised by JCB's agency Brookes & Vernons in the technical press over 21 years ago.

They are still pioneering innovative advertising and promotional campaigns for JCB 22 years after Cedric Brookes left JCB to set up his own advertising agency with JCB as his first client.

Brookes & Vernons has grown to be a leading communications group winning many awards for its work and JCB is still one of its major accounts today.

Special permission had to be obtained to take a JCB backhoe loader off-highway into the desert wilderness of Monument Valley, Utah for this 1978 photography session, shown on the right.

Customer requests for various attachments on the new 3CX
of 1980 resulted in the marketing of a special package, the
JCB 3CX Sitemaster of October 1981. Whilst others cut
back in the recession, JCB offered more and the Sitemaster
has become the company's best selling backhoe loader yet.
It features a 6 in 1 clamshovel with flip-over forks, and an
extending dipper with crane hook.

The 410 wheel loader of 1981 was part of a strategy to develop a market with smaller customers such as builders merchants, yet the articulated 410 also grew into other markets such as agriculture and was joined by the 415. The 410 was replaced in 1994 by the 1.1 cu m bucket capacity 411 and the 415 by the 1.3 cu m capacity 416.

To buy or grow your own ?   That is the question.

Organic growth is usually best, but there can be one drawback. The learning curve takes time to mature into profit.

JCB's probing of the quick alternative of buying in, is an interesting exercise in caution.

Few companies have the wallet for shopping sprees without bankers holding their hands. But with its financial strength and freedom JCB's name is usually whispered knowingly when construction equipment manufacturers have come up for sale. The opportunities to buy have always been there for the taking. But rarely does window shopping convert into a bargain buy.

This simple good sense has often been little understood by observers when the bargains have come along. Yes, JCB could have bought up dozens of manufacturers, like Horst Dieter Esch. With his I.B.H. empire he became for a few brief years in the early eighties the darling of German construction equipment manufacturing. JCB could also have borrowed and bought and borrowed and bought and gone bust by acquisition.

Instead of freedom to buy, top management at Rocester saw red alert.

Gilbert Johnston, chief executive from 1977 to 1992 and deputy Chairman until 1994 was Anthony Bamford's right hand man and helped steer the company through some of its most difficult times. Gilbert Johnston had often said: "We stick to the knitting, that's our strength." He often used this phrase to explain policy in presentations to the workforce.

Newspaper cartoonists found the idea of a possible tie up between JCB and Land Rover irresistible pickings in 1986.

Perhaps the most dramatic take-over-that-never-was concerned Land Rover in 1985 when JCB hit the headlines as a suitor. There was possible merit in a link between these two jewels of the off-highway world. It was not to be. Putting Land Rover back into shape could have put JCB under strain. Ultimately after lengthy consideration JCB didn't wish to take its eyes off the ball, to use another of Gilbert Johnston's favourite sayings, and was not disappointed when negotiations fell through.

Reticence to buy isn't dogma, but simply good sense. When the time is right, JCB will make a move. The company's first purchase was Chaseside Engineering of Blackburn in 1968. Established and respected, Chaseside manufactured loading shovels for a loyal customer base. Chaseside had gone from rope operation into hydraulics successfully enough but were stuck with a range of rigid chassis products.

Rocester was buying a stake in the loading shovel market. Production was moved to Rocester.

Chaseside had built largely one-offs to specific customer order, and volumes were low. Rocester had an eye to high volumes coupled with a new design - a machine with a chassis carrying the front axle and a chassis carrying the rear axle. With the two halves joined by an articulating joint the machine could ride rough ground and maintain ground contact through all four wheels at the same time. Such a

machine could also reverse and turn in a space much smaller than the old rigid designs.

Whilst this was not unique, the JCB approach certainly was - a cab mounted on the front module to give the driver best possible visibility of the load. The engine - and therefore the noise and the vibration - was mounted in the rear module. This unique approach won JCB a British Design Council award for innovation in 1974.

A JCB 413 wheel loader at work in 1979.

An 814 tracked excavator with extending Powerslide boom and a 712 dump truck in 1989. The 800 Series tracked machines have been superseded by the joint-venture JS range and the 700 Series dump trucks have been discontinued, as the market declined.

Treading Carefully

The Chaseside episode was successful in bringing new markets to Rocester. It also taught management how to tread carefully with acquisitions.

It also occurred at the time of JCB's attempt to buy Bamfords Limited of Uttoxeter.

The irony here is the eventual purchase of the Bamfords Ltd Uttoxeter premises. This is now the ideal location for an ambitious joint venture - JCB-SCM.

The first product of JCB-SCM was a 20 tonne JS 200 tracked excavator honoured by a roll out ceremony by the entire workforce on 17 December 1992.

Here is proof enough of willingness to change, whilst at the same time 'sticking to the knitting'.

By the late eighties JCB very much wanted to take its 800 Series tracked machines forward. A well developed marketing expertise and the substantial distributor network throughout Europe and beyond was already in place. But success was hampered. There was no wheeled excavator line. Traditionally wheeled machines had markets throughout Europe with the exception of the UK which in general preferred tracked machines. Whilst prototype wheeled machines had been built over 20 years ago the company had been reluctant to commit to production in the absence of a UK market. Now, that market was growing, and JCB did not want to lose out. Besides, the market was changing due to the rapidly increasing repair work on urban roads and motorways.

Wheeled machines were being increasingly seen as ideal for congested areas where they could get to site under their own power, not needing expensive low loaders and not causing damage to the road surface.

One option was the JCB tradition - pump investment into development. The downside of this was time.

The JCB-SCM joint venture has brought JCB into the wheeled excavator market with the JS 130W and JS 150W.

Meanwhile, Japan's Sumitomo Construction Machinery Co Ltd (SCM) was looking for ways of breaking into the European market and saw JCB's strength in marketing and distribution.

The scene was set. Experience, confidence, and sound business sense for partnership were in place on both sides. JCB-SCM was created following the signing of agreements in March 1991. JCB owns 51%. The Japanese partners are Sumitomo and Itochu.

The following month work began in the Uttoxeter factory, preparing the run up to production.

This joint-venture has been a remarkable achievement. Since production of that first JS 200 in December 1992 , four tracked models have gone into production - JS 130, JS 150 LC, JS 200 LC, JS 300 LC. There are also two wheeled models, the JS 130 W and JS 150 W.

The JCB-SCM team has been led from the start of the project by managing director Alan Mellor, formerly JCB's finance director. There is no doubt that this joint venture formula is producing the most successful hydraulic excavators ever to carry the JCB name.

Another tracked machine, the JS 240 LC will go into production before the end of this JCB Jubilee Year.

The first of the JCB JS range of excavators was produced at Uttoxeter in December 1992.

Cultural Change

By the end of 1994 the factory had produced its 1000th local content machine, a fascinating event for those interested in cultural change.

Picture the scene; here is Britain's most well-known and successful family-owned engineering company. Here is a workforce with a clear sense of identity if there ever was one. JCB is no place for nostalgia.

The philosophy has been single minded. The Uttoxeter production line is identical to Sumitomo's Chiba factory in Japan. The machine tools are the same. The robot welders run computer programs which have also run identical robots at Chiba.

Six of the 250 employees are Japanese. They give help and advice, and act as the interface with the Chiba factory to ensure nothing is lost in translation.

Currently 80% of the content is produced at Uttoxeter. Japan supplies hydraulics and Isuzu engines.

Current investment tops £10m and this has laid in place realistic production targets of 12 machines a day. JCB-SCM shares half the 281,750 sq ft factory with JCB Special Products. In July 1995 Special Products move to their new home outside the nearby town of Cheadle. When that happens, the entire Uttoxeter factory will be turned over to JCB-SCM.

The JCB-SCM success is not, however, JCB's first joint venture.

That title goes to Escorts JCB Ltd , India. The Escorts JCB joint venture was signed on 13th February 1979 with Escorts Ltd, one of India's largest and most respected engineering manufacturing groups. Escorts completed 50 years of operation in 1994 and is very similar to JCB as it began in a small way, and grew extensively under the control of the Nanda family.

The objective for Escorts JCB was to build a locally produced backhoe loader. Because of India's stringent import restrictions export from Rocester was impossible. With import licences hard to get no market as such existed despite a crying need. Negotiations were set in place by the late Bert Ballin, JCB's international sales director at the time. Bert was known to the Nanda family from his earlier dealings with them over Massey Ferguson tractors before his JCB days.

Manufacturing began in 1980 from a 23 acre factory at Ballabgarh, 30 km from New Delhi. Economic reforms in India since 1992 have been extremely beneficial to Escorts JCB and it is expected company turnover will continue to grow. Expansion is planned beyond the current product range of 72 and 92 hp excavator loaders, 127 hp articulated loading shovel, 72 hp front end loader, and JCB 530 Loadall.

A number of JCB managers have been involved in the growth of the business.

One is Jim Edwards, who helped set up the new production lines in his time there to 1985. Today Jim is managing director of JCB Special Products.

1995, Anthony Bamford lays the foundation stone for the new manufacturing hall at Escorts JCB. Pictured left to right: Derek Pells, technical manager EJCB, Dr Virendra Singh, deputy general manager HRD EJCB, P Rao, senior divisional manager Parts and Service EJCB, John Sandland, financial controller JCB Rocester, Surinder Lal, union representative EJCB, Tim Leadbeater, commercial director JCB, John Patterson, managing director JCB Sales, Anthony and Carole Bamford, Arvind Agrawal, executive director EJCB, Vijay Sharma, general manager EJCB, Eash Jaitly general manager sales EJCB.

Left to right sitting, EJCB divisional managers: I J Dulloo, materials, R Dayal, Sales, J Sharma, product engineering, A Seth, corporate affairs, G Dhobal, production, H Mohan, loading shovels.

A JCB project team on a visit to Escorts JCB, India in November 1981. Left to right, Escorts group finance director C K Hazari, JCB commercial director Tim Leadbeater, Rajan Nanda, Anthony Bamford, and JCB project leader Campbell Reid.

Pictured here at a reception to mark Escorts fiftieth anniversary are Sir Anthony and Lady Bamford with Anil Nanda (left) vice Chairman Escorts Ltd and his brother Rajan Nanda, Chairman and managing director. Their father Mr H P Nanda, Chairman Emeritus, founded the company. Escorts Ltd completed 50 years of operations in 1994. A team from Rocester led by Anthony and Carole Bamford visited the Escorts JCB factory at Ballabgarh in February 1995 to see the 3,500th backhoe loader roll off the production line.

Fostering Ownership Within Teams

JCB has always believed in the talents to be found within its workforce. Since 1990 the company has been taking even more substantial actions to tap deeper into the skills and experience of its employees.

In order to improve performance the company has been restructured into smaller decision-making business units. At the same time the change of culture has been addressed through a tailor-made TQM programme - Total Quality Management - which is called Complete Customer Quality - CCQ for short. The idea is that everyone is treated as an important customer, both inside and outside the company.

Anthony Bamford had felt that real progress could be made by accelerating the process of change. As chief executive and then deputy chairman Gilbert Johnston championed this idea, and before his retirement the CCQ process was well established. The new chief executive Martin Coyne has built on the successes and added to the concept of divisionalisation.

Coyne, formerly at Rocester as purchasing director and then managing director of JCB Service, had taken over as managing director at JCB Hydrapower Ltd, Rugeley, to oversee the development of the mini excavator range.

The backhoe loader assembly line in 1995 currently rolls out 50 machines a day. Each machine is built to individual distributor order and is paid for at time of despatch, a principle which Joe Bamford learned from Ford in the early fifties. He would drive his Commer lorry to buy skid units six at a time from Ford with a cheque in his pocket.

Martin Coyne - chief executive

He had established design and manufacturing of these machines and personally experienced the benefits of everyone in the company identifying with the single product, and their sense of ownership in a small company.

It was this experience which was to be reflected in the reconstruction into single-product business units elsewhere in the group.

Twenty years ago JCB had three main products manufactured at one factory - the Rocester plant. The most dominant was the Backhoe Loader which represented well over 90% of sales at the time.

Product Focus

Many of these machines have been developed in the last six years, and following their successful launch new factories have been established within a few miles of the main Rocester plant at Cheadle, Uttoxeter, and Rugeley.

Because 'ownership' has been addressed from a structural standpoint the artificial barriers of design, manufacturing and marketing have been broken down. Each division now reports its own performance, sales turnover and profit each month to the Executive board. Each product therefore has a higher profile than ever before.

Better performance led to the introduction in 1994 of JCB's profit-related pay scheme which gave each UK employee a £700 tax-free bonus at Christmas, and a further payout of £206 at Easter 1995.

The tailored CCQ initiative has been the biggest contributor in changing the culture.

Alan Fernyhough, personnel director: "This whole process has created far more openness and each quarter we survey 20% of our employees in each business unit on five major factors of performance."

These are: goals and objectives, leadership style, cost of waste, process review, projects.

Fernyhough: "Many more employees see their work not as a routine job but as a place where they can contribute, achieve, and use their creative skills in an enthusiastic way. Just one small measurement of our success has been that suggestions into our suggestion scheme have increased tenfold in the last two years."

"The culture in which our business units operate is changing. We are developing a leadership style which is harnessing the talent we have in the company. Either as teams or as individuals we are trying to improve competence throughout the organisation."

Fernyhough keeps a message in his office and often likes to remind himself of its simplicity.

It reads:" The only source of lasting competitive advantage is our ability to develop and release the full potential of people better than our competitors."

Today the product range has widened, and the market share and product volumes have increased. As a result the backhoe loader is still market leader in its own right, but as a proportion of the new range it now represents less than 50% of total sales.

The product range now includes, besides backhoe loaders, wheeled loading shovels, Loadalls, rough terrain forklift trucks, mini excavators, Robot skid steers, Fastracs, and the joint venture JS range of tracked and wheeled excavators.

Landscaped, And Set in 95 Acres.

Jim Edwards sat waiting his turn. Those before him had gone in hopefully but exited glumly, their planning applications for garages and loft extensions and the like rejected.

Staffordshire Moorlands District Planning committee was in session and Edwards with his carefully prepared proposal was getting increasingly anxious.

He wanted rather more than a garage. He wanted permission to build a factory.

Edwards: "When our turn came we were really tense. We waited as the Chairman called for the show of hands by those in favour. Everyone put up a hand. It was one hundred per cent. Just wonderful. This shows what tremendous support there is from the council for JCB. And this is what the people of Cheadle think of us."

And so began the move by JCB Special Products Ltd for their new factory on the outskirts of the town. There is industrial planning permission confirmed on 75 acres and another 20 acres has been purchased to assist landscaping in the JCB style.

From a distance the Cheadle plant echoes the clean lines of JCB Rocester. But the four production bays and the glass frontage focal point are lower. The reason is that Cheadle is the new home for small compact equipment.

The term 'compact' embraces the small machines which are designed and manufactured by JCB Special Products.

Also it includes mini excavators produced by JCB Hydrapower at Rugeley.

JCB Special Products launched the innovative 2CX backhoe loader in 1990. The spur was customer demand for something smaller and nippier than the 3CX. With growing urban congestion, highway repair work needed to be done within a single lane closure.

In 1985 Anthony Bamford had the idea of setting up a small group to look at producing special machines. The idea grew and so did the team. This is the new 1995 Cheadle development for JCB Special Products with Jim Edwards, managing director, and the ICX.

Meanwhile over at Rugeley, JCB Hydrapower had broken into the growing mini tracked excavator market with the 801 in 1989. This class of machine, easy to transport on the back of a small trailer and easy to operate, gained a substantial UK market share in its first full year.

Once again JCB was not slow in learning lessons and taking action to run with market demands. The result has been substantial growth to cope with demand. Under managing director Howard McCallum, JCB Hydrapower is increasing production capacity still further in 1995.

The 801 success taught JCB much and it was reasoned that a small backhoe loader could bite into the same territory. The strengths of the conventional JCB backhoe loader - loader performance to rival a dedicated loading shovel and a backhoe equalling dedicated tracked excavators - did not apply. Customers were typically digging no further than a metre. What was needed increasingly was a sturdy little runabout capable of serious work.

Shorter, narrower, with four equal sized wheels and four wheel steer the 2CX broke all production estimates. As before, action to fill a gap in the market resulted in a whole new

market. With its full sized cab , another point learned well from the JCB 801, the 2CX has grown to become a significant export revenue earner.

JCB mini excavators are manufactured at the JCB Hydrapower factory in Rugeley. The first machine was produced in 1989 and there is now a range of six models. The product strategy is to build minis to high quality levels, and with comfortable spacious cabs despite the small size of the machines.

Safety First

It is impossible to record the introduction of any JCB product without also recording innovation. Sometimes it isn't difficult to see links right back to the earliest years.

Similarities in thinking between the Sidraulic loader of 1953 and the JCB Robot of 1993 are substantial. For example, the Sidraulic used a single arm to the left of the tractor driver. The benefit was clear access from the right. Similarly the JCB Robot uses a single loader arm to the right of the operator, and this has allowed a fully enclosed cab design and an access door from the left.

Bearing in mind the safety conscious 1990's, it is salutary to think just how far ahead of his time Mr Bamford was in the 1950's as an innovative designer. JCB came late to the established skid steer market after considering a variety of options during the eighties. The company held back because there was a missing ingredient. That was how to give the operator a side access door which could be accessed easily and safely.

Major players in the tractor market had spurned full suspension and it took JCB as complete outsiders to offer it with Fastrac. Virtually at the same time as the first Fastracs went into production, JCB was inventive again in an entirely different market.

The JCB Robot has brought innovation to a market previously thought to be mature in product design. The side entry door offers safety and comfort, all made possible by the single arm design.

In terms of design focus JCB saw a problem with the generally well accepted skid steer. What nagged away was the issue of safety.

Conventionally it is necessary to climb in over the front, but that is where the control levers are typically situated. With lift arms either side of the machine, and engine to the rear, there is no other way in or out. And this is the Achilles heel which so worried JCB. Until it could be solved JCB would not enter the market.

Almost all accidents with machinery are due to operator misuse born of over familiarity, cutting corners, and plain carelessness. Conventional "front entry" skid steers have system lock-outs, safety procedures, even skull and crossbones signs to get the message across. Yet hair raising reports of accidents abound.

This then, was the background to JCB entering the well established skid steer market late in the day. This is a story of how an outsider can bring in something new when major players either cannot or will not. In this sense the Fastrac and the Robot are classic examples of how to rattle the closed doors of convention.

Unusual Company

JCB has managed to balance the need for profit with a desire to innovate for the benefit of customers. It is this which is its true character; both historically and for the future.

The backhoe loader is the machine which has sustained the company's growth, the machine which is to construction what Hoover is to vacuum cleaning. Yet, true to corporate character, it is the machine which the company has tried to change most.

Anyone trying to challenge the foundation product in most companies would indeed be brave, perhaps even foolhardy. But just such a man went off at a tangent at JCB Special Products and had Anthony Bamford and Joe Bamford listening. He saw his idea turned into full production, rather than his career card marked.

To understand the significance of the ICX, the smallest true backhoe loader ever produced, it is necessary to go further back than its launch in the spring of 1994. Further back even than the day in 1991 that 27 year old development engineer Pat Naylor looked at a prototype JCB Robot skid steer, and thought it could be adapted and turned around to make a compact backhoe loader.

Right back to 1985 in fact. Jim Edwards returned to Rocester after setting up the production lines for the Escorts JCB factory in India. The backhoe loader assembly line had its hands full, as ever, coping with worldwide product variants. Take any handful of consecutive machines 'on build' any time and it will be rare to find any two with the same build specification. Such is the complexity and responsiveness to customer demand.

Putting added burden of so called 'sales specials' into the daily mix was turning on the pressure too much. This gave Anthony Bamford cause for concern as opportunities to respond to customer requirements were being missed. He asked Edwards to set up a new business to look at satisfying the need for "sales specials". The two discussed the possibilities and Anthony's idea for JCB Special Products was born.

Edwards: "We knew that it needed to be an unusual company, with people in it who would thrive on the unusual. We needed designers who could literally design off the back of a cigarette packet, and people who could just go and make it."

"We used to say to everybody 'Whatever your question is, the answer is yes' and we've since had a hell of a good time."

According to Edwards, who himself began in the Rocester drawing office in 1965, designs almost never come from just one person. As managing director of JCB Special Products he brims with an engaging enthusiasm for new ideas and production, and is rarely seen there in a suit. Even in the office, he is happiest in the practical blue overalls of the shop floor.

Edwards: "Designs usually develop between the team. You tend to get to where you're going to by a series of friendly rows across the table."

His other observation is that his designers - he calls them 'concepters' - need to be able to make things and not just draw. "The whole design industry has all gone CAD and you can do magic things. But here you have to be able to feel it, touch it, walk all the way around it and sit in it."

The hydrostatic drive JCB 1CX backhoe loader was launched to European distributors at a strategy conference in Malaga in the spring of 1994. It is part of a new concentration on compact equipment. Design and manufacturing teams at Uttoxeter developed the machine into production following a top management decision to proceed with the 1991 idea of a young development engineer.

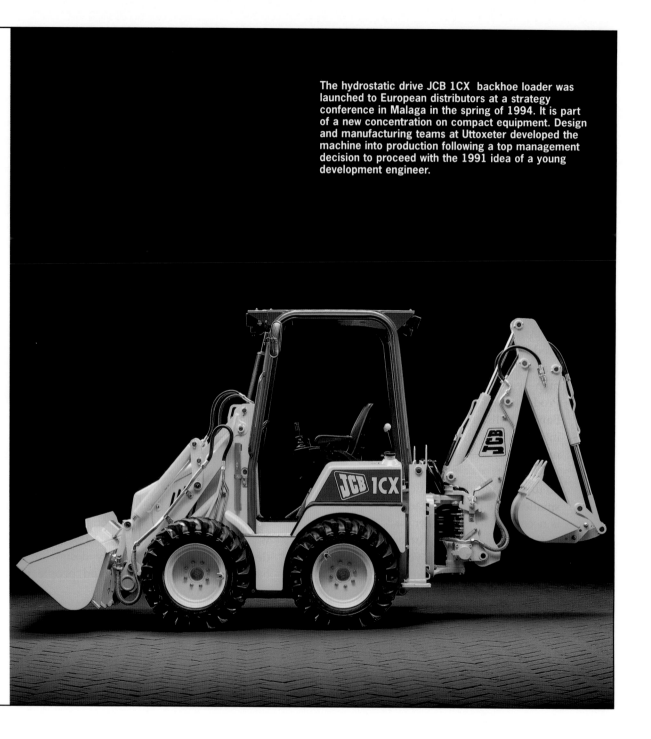

It was this culture which led to Pat Naylor coming up with the idea for making a backhoe loader out of a Robot skid steer. Naylor could see the possibilities. Edwards allocated a Robot development chassis to be cut and carved. Naylor and fitter Rob Gunn took a cutting torch and sliced everything off above the fender line.

Two days later in May 1991 they had a mock up sitting there on the skid steer chassis made with plywood, cardboard, and plastic drainpipe cut to represent hydraulic rams. This was the beginning of another world first at JCB. When the JCB Robot was finished, other teams of specialists set to work on the 1CX as resource was diverted to the project.

The first visual mock up 1CX which was put together over two days in May 1991. Everything below the fender line was a development skid steer. Everything above was plywood, cardboard and plastic drainpipe. The chassis was cut up in 1994 so that parts could be cannibalised to try out more ideas.

The JCB Robot has brought the new dimension of safety to the skid steer market. Yet even before launch it sparked off ideas for a new concept, the ICX backhoe loader.

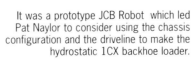

It was a prototype JCB Robot which led Pat Naylor to consider using the chassis configuration and the driveline to make the hydrostatic 1CX backhoe loader.

A Worldwide Organisation

One of the principles of JCB is concentration on product development, engineering and manufacturing excellence. Yet management is the first to admit that it is the independent worldwide distributor network which has been the backbone of the success.

It has been a firm policy to encourage independent distributors by providing the products and support with which to compete effectively. There are two sides to this focus, machines and parts.

Marketing, sales and supply of new machines is handled by JCB Sales Ltd in major markets.

Both sales and service functions work closely together and are headed up by JCB Sales and Service managing director John Patterson, who has been with JCB since 1971.

There are subsidiary companies in the major markets of North America, France, Germany, Italy and The Netherlands. Spain is the newest established in 1993.

There are also regional branch offices in Denmark, Cyprus, South Africa, Brazil, Colombia, Mexico, Australia, Singapore and Hong Kong.

JCB Service operates through these same subsidiaries and regional offices to provide sales and marketing support for service and parts. The JCB branding of proprietary components and consumables such as oils, filters and batteries has been instrumental in making the independent JCB distributor network the recognised focus for all aspects of customer care.

October 1975, Mrs Marjorie Bamford inaugurates new building work for JCB France, watched by Michael Heseltine MP, Mr JC Bamford CBE, and Pierre Leboucher, of JCB France

JCB Landpower at Cheadle

information for JCB dealers in the UK and around the world.

Twenty years ago the majority of the Parts Division's work was to supply repair parts but as machines become more reliable and longer lived, this is a declining part of the business. A growing part of the business is the sale of attachments. More than 2,000 attachments are offered covering the whole of JCB's extensive range of machines.

Consumables and branded product lines have been a real success. JCB now sells everything from batteries, oils and lubricants, to tyres and tracks. There is also the JCB range of merchandise, such as models, hats and coats, which are always popular.

JCB was the first construction equipment manufacturer to offer an electronic vehicle tracking system on its machines - the JCB Tracker unit. Tracker is an example of how the Parts Division is continually looking to broaden the options.

With the most widespread distributor network of any construction equipment manufacturer in the UK, JCB has a spread of 46 depots offering parts and service support cover.

Since exporting began in the early fifties JCB has pursued a policy of encouraging distributors through regular daily contact and support direct with the customer.

The parts centre at Rocester covers 230,000 square feet and the parts warehouse stocks 50,000 items.

To meet demand from customers on all five continents 80,000 items are despatched each week. That's 26 items per minute.

JCB is adopting modern information technology to achieve faster customer service. Parts and service information is being put on to CD ROM to provide a single source of

JCB SA, France

JCB-SCM at Uttoxeter

There are nearly 500 factory trained engineers working within the distributor organisation all of whom are kept fully trained on all of the JCB products.

JCB has a £2 million training facility - the JCB International Training Centre - at Woodseat, close to the Rocester headquarters. It is a purpose designed centre with four workshops and six lecture rooms with state of the art equipment.

It's a prerequisite that all distribution staff are job trained. Last year 1,600 passed through the doors at Woodseat Training Centre.

Lecturers from the JCB International Training Centre also travel overseas organising and carrying out on-territory training for the company's dealers.

And in Sarcelles, near Paris, JCB has a top class training facility for mainland Europe where training courses are organised.

JCB Transmissions at Wrexham

JCB NV, The Netherlands

JCB Baumaschinen und Industriemaschinen, Germany

JCB Hydrapower, Rugeley

JCB Inc. USA

Escorts JCB, India

The 1995 JCB Loadall range consists of 12 models and the concept of versatile telescopic boom machines is well accepted in construction, agriculture and general industry. But before the first JCB 520 Telescopic Handler was introduced in 1977 the benefits of forward reach in efficient materials handling were not appreciated. An intensive marketing campaign was begun by JCB to change established thinking.

CHAPTER FOUR

Major challenges to conventional thinking

A New Way of Doing Things

JCB has taught itself much about the benefits of re-grouping into dedicated teams with a product focus. The earliest examples are from the late seventies.

JCB Transmissions, established in 1978, built JCB Max-Trac axles to begin with. Its principal working structure has been to operate independently, and to negotiate contracts with the Rocester purchasing department just like any other outside supplier. JCB Transmissions supplies JCB components, and with its other hat - International Transmissions - actively seeks non-JCB customers worldwide.

The factory is on the Wrexham Industrial Estate, and therefore geographically furthest away from Rocester.

JCB Transmissions' business is the design, manufacture, sale and product support for transmissions and axles for on/off highway vehicles.

In 1978 there were less than a dozen employees and now there are 320.

Production quality has been acknowledged through numerous awards, including the Machinery Award for Innovation in Production Engineering as a result of quality improvement and significant cost savings brought about by the use of new tooling.

A completely different approach was taken at the same time with JCB Materials Handling. This was a marketing division within the main sales and marketing function of JCB Sales. Run by former UK sales director Jim Harrison and later Mike Butler it was briefed to operate rather like a commando squad; find opportunities, break rules, develop new policies. So much so that it once held a product launch conference with members of the team conducting army-style briefings to the distributor sales force whilst dressed in combat gear.

Its first product was the highly innovative JCB 520 Telescopic Handler. Smaller than the North American machines which had given JCB the original idea, it was aimed initially at European construction. Here, the principle of forward reach was unknown. In the same way that the backhoe loader had been developed in the early fifties when Europe was crying out for mechanised muck shifting and trench digging, so too the telescopic handler was developed at a time when labour and material costs were soaring.

In the fifties the backhoe loader's main competition was the pick and shovel. In the late seventies the competition for the telescopic handler was manual labour such as hod carrying up ladders.

Telescopic reach machines were originally an American idea spotted by Mr Bamford in the early seventies, and then scaled down for the European market with the launch of the JCB 520 Telescopic Handler in October 1977. That original 520 has evolved into the 12 model JCB Loadall range of today. This example was photographed in 1994 at work in the USA.

Hard Fought Battles

With the principle of forward reach largely unknown, JCB had to hard sell the concept. It was necessary to change existing ways of working on site. Success would come only as a result of hard fought battles, and in October 1977 advertising for the original JCB 520 Telescopic Handler took on the world.

JCB quickly had to learn a hard lesson that the only way forward would be in four wheel drive format, and soon the two wheel drive model was dropped.

The JCB Telescopic Handler range grew so successful that the name which JCB had invented - telescopic handler - was becoming generic in the industry, and this is true today. This is why JCB was so willing to change its own name. JCB Loadall is a name with full pedigree right back to 1958, when it was used to describe the front loader on the JCB Hydra Digga. It was also a registered name which cannot be used by others.

The JCB Loadall range quickly became JCB's second highest volume product to the backhoe loader, a position it holds to this day. JCB Materials Handling has evolved into the JCB Loadall Division of today, responsible for design, purchase, manufacturing and marketing. There are currently 12 models, all telescopic. The smallest is the 520-55, with 2 tonne lift capacity to 5.5m and the largest is the 537 - 130 which will take 3.7 tonne to 13m.

The JCB Loadall range is world market leader, well accepted in construction, agriculture and general industry.

The challenge to established thinking, methods and working practices on sites had worked. The battle was won.

The JCB Loadall range is the world leader. This Loadall is at work in agriculture where the combination of four wheel drive, forward reach and also reach at height makes the JCB Loadall equally as versatile as it is in construction.

Mini Excavator Production Leads The Way

In the late eighties JCB entered into a short-lived agreement to build mini excavators with Kubota running gear. Before the project was shelved it had fired the imagination of Martin Coyne, managing director of JCB Service at the time, who was convinced JCB must build its own machines in its own way.

Also, Coyne had been responsible for JCB Hydrapower Ltd, a small division producing hydraulic power packs, a business JCB have been involved with since 1980. He was convinced there was great potential.

Giving up his JCB Service role to concentrate on the new focus of smaller machines, Coyne convinced Anthony Bamford to allow him to begin afresh. Today that idea has grown into an autonomous factory at Rugeley, and a workforce of 180 people.

This has been an astonishing growth from a standing start in just a few short years. Confirmation of JCB Hydrapower's success came in 1994 with a Queen's Award for Export Achievement.

Its first product was the 801, a 1.5 tonne machine which went into production in late 1989 at Rugeley. In 1995 there are six models.

The original core of the company, JCB Hydrochief hydraulic power packs, is also a successful division employing 25 people.

JCB Hydrapower has operated as an almost completely autonomous company, with only a few services from Rocester. Its product strategy has been to build mini excavators to very high quality levels, and with comfortable roomy cabs. The autonomy of the company and its small size has enabled it to innovate in its systems, production and assembly methods. It has also spearheaded JCB's focus on the growing compact equipment market in Europe.

This is the compact equipment line up of 1995.

JCB has maintained its investment in new product development throughout the recessions of the early eighties and early nineties and this has undoubtedly put the company in a strong position for achieving future ambitions.

For some time now a strategy has been developing based on competing in eight product groups. Since the Malaga conference of March 1994 this strategy has been firmly set in place. Wheeled loaders continue to be the largest product group in Europe and therefore JCB is giving increasing attention to improving its share.

New Focus on Shovels

The divisionalisation of the existing product ranges is complete. Even the backhoe loader product range is looked after by its own team. The JCB Backhoe Loader Division operates in much the same way as does the Loadall Division. For a mature product which has been improved continuously since the mid fifties, there is still much to do as far as JCB is concerned. The latest focus is on the operator environment.

The newest product type to come under the spotlight is the wheeled loader. The Wheeled Loader Division was formed in March 1993 under the leadership of former purchasing director John Appleby with its own teams for design, marketing and a production line within the Rocester factory.

There are five products, and like the Backhoe Loader Division, the focus is very firmly on the operator's environment. There is a tradition of continuity, and some of those working on today's machines came to JCB in the 1968 takeover of Chaseside.

The Great Indoors

The JCB 3CX backhoe loader is a classic of modern design now enhanced by improvements to cab comfort and safety. The focus owes much to automotive comfort and little to traditional construction equipment.

In-cab noise level is the lowest on the market at 74 dBA. Heating and demisting is 60% more powerful than previous models. Also factory fitted air-conditioning is available. Controls, switches and instrumentation have all been relocated for improved ergonomics.

There are recessed compartments to store personal items neatly and there is even a place for a cup and flask.

An adjustable suspension swivel seat provides lumbar support. It is fully reclining, is available with armrests and headrest, and a safety belt is standard. There is also a clock, and power steering with an adjustable tilt steering wheel.

The new cab is fitted across the 3CX and 4CX range. Greater demand for productivity and operator comfort has turned JCB's attention to four-wheel-steer and four-wheel-drive, a combination marketed along with four equal sized wheels in the JCB 4CX Sitemaster. This top-of-the-range model offers three choices of steer mode to cope with extremes of ground condition. The operator may select from all-wheel steer, front wheel steer, and four wheel 'crab' steer.

The range offers high performance from other features such as:

- JCB Syncro Shuttle or Powershift gearbox with torque converter and reversing shuttle.
- Four wheel drive with electrical disconnect on-the-move to two wheel drive for roading.
- Hydraulic speed control for either loader performance or transmission power.
- JCB Hitchmaster for changing attachments to the excavator in just a few seconds.
- Dual hydraulic pumps allow the Extradig extending dipper and excavator to operate simultaneously.

All these features of today's design inter-relate to make the operator's working day more comfortable and more productive than has ever been possible before.

These machines were photographed in October 1994 on the construction site for the new JCB Special Products factory at Cheadle.

105

The Development of Fastrac.

With the Fastrac, JCB introduced the world's first genuine high speed tractor with full suspension.

JCB Fastracs are a range of tractors covering the 120 hp to 160 plus hp categories. The concept is unique because a Fastrac can be driven on the road at up to 75 kph (45 mph) and yet it is immediately ready to go off-road and plough equally as well as a conventional tractor. Visually it is unconventional too, with a truck-type cab for the driver and a passenger to sit side by side.

Fastrac is one of the true world-class greats in farm machinery design. It owes its uniqueness to full suspension operating on both axles. At the front conventional coil springs with twin tube telescopic shock absorbers suspend the front axle. At the rear is a hydro-pneumatic suspension system which automatically maintains the chassis level with self levelling.

Fastracs are manufactured at a dedicated factory in Cheadle, Staffordshire, by JCB Landpower Ltd. This company was created specifically for Fastrac production, marketing, sales and service in 1989 during the run up to commercial production.

It took over from JCB Developments based next to the JCB Transmissions factory at Wrexham. JCB Developments had taken the original concept through design and prototype testing. This was effectively a joint effort run by Neil Bedford, at the time also managing director of JCB Transmissions Ltd, and Mike Butler, managing director of JCB Materials Handling.

Bedford oversaw all the engineering development and Butler marketing. When production went 'live' in 1990 Butler was managing director of JCB Landpower Ltd during the start-up phase, after which he handed over to the current managing director David Bell.

A Simple Idea

JCB Landpower Ltd now employs over 100 and has chiefly concentrated since launch on bringing Fastracs to agricultural markets. This special expertise has also brought responsibility for marketing other appropriate JCB products into agriculture, and these include the Loadalls, and smaller articulated loaders.

JCB Landpower Ltd is responsible for on-going development, production, marketing, and sales and service support to distributors.

The project began years earlier when Anthony Bamford was enjoying a holiday overseas. He had been turning over the idea of manufacturing a new type of tractor which would have higher road speed than conventional tractors and might also incorporate elements of truck design such as suspension. He picked up the telephone to call JCB Transmissions and put the idea to Neil Bedford. Before moving to JCB Transmissions Bedford had been manufacturing director at Foden Trucks.

Bedford: " The call came right out of the blue. Anthony said he had this idea for a fast tractor and would I get onto it. Together with Tony Wrathall I looked at what else was around at the time and we came to the

Mike Butler, now managing director of the JCB Loadall Division, was managing director of JCB Landpower as Fastrac developed from a secret project through to full production.

conclusion that the other applications of suspension were diabolical. We were convinced we should have a go ourselves."

"I was very busy with the transmission business at the time but I told Anthony that we would like to have a go. I also said that we would like to have suspension all round. It was all a very exciting time really."

The first prototypes were built in secret underneath the office block at JCB Transmissions. Meanwhile Butler and his marketing team had already taken on the task of finding out what farmers wanted.

By September 1984 the idea was forming for some kind of versatile road runabout. Butler pursued the idea to the extent of setting up a technical panel of farmers. He was determined that should anything come to fruition it would be shaped by customer opinion.

By early 1986 Mike Butler and Neil Bedford knew here was the possibility of a machine which could take advantage of existing componentry in its make up. The market was keen, and it would add a valuable new dimension to JCB's product portfolio.

The concept was shaping into a tractor which had full suspension, but the technical panel of farmers insisted that to stand any chance of being taken seriously it must be able to plough.

This was indeed a challenge. Conventional wisdom trotted out by major tractor manufacturers held that suspension is to ploughing what chalk is to cheese.

This polarised view had held sway for generations. Yet standing alone was not new to JCB.

Standing Alone

When JCB decides to move, it generally moves very fast. A strong chief engineer was needed, and over in Manchester at MF Industrial, just such a man had overseen the development of the MF 50H and MF 30H backhoe loaders. David Brown, 39 years old and ready for a fresh challenge left MF and joined the project in June 1986.

Butler's initial marketing specification was being prepared whilst Brown was being headhunted, and the document was ready by the end of May. Within three weeks the top secret 'Project 130' began with a confidential meeting on June 19th 1986, held to lay the parameters for project control.

Project 130 was the development code name for what was to become the highly successful Fastrac range of today.

Besides Brown, an invaluable addition to the team was Ray Clay, who joined in February 1987 from Bedford Trucks. He is one of the world's leading authorities on the design of automotive suspension systems and the relationship between suspension and traction.

One of the strengths of Fastrac has been that the original design team is still on the project. Besides Brown and Clay they include Tony Moore, test manager, and Tony Wrathall, engineering director at JCB Transmissions, Wrexham.

There was little over a year between that initial project control meeting and the first 'roll out' of prototype number one. It took place on 30th October 1987 at a disused airfield in Cheshire, well away from prying eyes.

Anxious to try out their new baby, Brown, Clay and Moore each took the wheel. The world's first real tractor with full suspension was off.

JCB Fastracs on the assembly line in February 1995.

Detail showing the concept of the Fastrac which went into full commercial production at the JCB Landpower factory, Cheadle, in May 1991. This is the world's first genuine high speed tractor with full suspension. Front suspension comprises conventional coil springs, with twin tube telescopic shock absorbers mounted in front of the axle. Rear suspension is self-levelling, ensuring the chassis always rides at the same height above the rear axle, regardless of loads.

One of the considerations in developing a tractor is that it takes a year to assess each task in the farming calendar just once. The only way to shorten the development time of Fastrac was to build a number of evaluation machines and have them all out working through the seasons. This grey cab machine is prototype 1 (P1) which was the first 'in the iron' machine to run. Roll out was October 1987. Others went to France, Germany, Australia, and Southern Africa. P14 was the public launch machine at the Smithfield Show in November 1990.

One of the early names for Fastrac was HMV - high mobility vehicle. Here is the development team at Wrexham in May 1989. Missing from the photo is suspension expert and project manager Ray Clay, who took the photograph. Left to right standing: Richard Jones, test driver; Chris Bickle, test driver; Richard Cole, development engineer; Dave Brown, chief engineer; Mike Butler, managing director JCB Materials Handling; Neil Bedford, managing director JCB Transmissions; Ken Bradley, Project consultant; Andrew Bellchambers, materials handling sales team; Ian Shields, UK agricultural sales; Tony Wrathall, director of engineering JCB Transmissions.
Top: Ivan Tatt, marketing manager; Tony Moore, senior development engineer JCB Transmissions; Paul Owen, workshop supervisor.

Exploding The Myth

Mike Butler: "We very quickly realised that we had something very special indeed. The ride qualities were outstanding. The next milestone was finding we could plough. Conventional wisdom was that you couldn't do draft work with a suspended axle. We tried it and found that you could. The old myth had been exploded."

David Brown and his team had gingerly fitted up a two furrow plough just to see if ploughing were possible at all. The first time they ploughed it was on the 75 acre test site at Plumpton, two miles from Rocester. On that first day with the plough they unearthed a rusty old horseshoe. David Brown has that lucky horseshoe to this day.

The only way to shorten the development time was to build a number of evaluation prototypes and have them all out working on test through the seasons.

By the time a prototype Fastrac was unveiled at the Smithfield Show in November 1990 the development project had cost £12 million.

Butler: "When we started we thought we had found a niche, but this is not a niche market at all. It could turn out to be the most important development in agricultural machinery since Harry Ferguson put a three point linkage on the back of his tractor."

The first finished machine. It is interesting that Fastrac uses no revolutionary technology. It is simply the way it is all put together that works so well. For example, Fastrac has benefitted from developments such as the Bosch electronic draft control. Also tyre companies were beginning to look at high speed tyres coincidentally during Fastrac development.

CHAPTER FIVE

Measures of success throughout fifty years

Jamais Content Bamford

As Inventive and Enthusiastic as ever

By 1975 Mr JC Bamford had established his company as one of the United Kingdom's great success stories of the post war era.

JCB was increasingly known at home and abroad. Now, he judged it time to retire and hand over to Anthony, who was to lead the company further forward.

Yet Mr Bamford was to be as inventive and enthusiastic as ever - even in retirement. He was interviewed for this book on 22 December 1994.

During the day important clues to his philosophy and style became evident.

The first clue is to do with learning. Mr JCB wants to learn something every day.

The second clue is about having fun. This may come as a surprise to those who imagine engineers and engineering to be dull. It will come as no surprise to those who saw the boss roaring around the office on a scooter. This example was in the early seventies before he retired. Those who saw him waving excitedly as he sped down the drawing office still smile fondly at the memory.

Hard Lessons

These clues are examples of the way in which he watched, learned, and had fun building his international company based on sound economic sense.

He never forgot any lesson. And it was the hard lessons that shaped his approach to business most of all.

Let's start with the reason behind JCB being always profitable, self financing, and never borrowing money:

"I never borrowed money except on one occasion, and that was when we were still at Crakemarsh. There was a credit squeeze and on the Monday the bank manager said I had until Friday to find the money. I resolved never to be put in that position ever again.

Too many people have had the rug pulled from under them in that way, particularly in the last five years or so."

Factory visitors unconnected with JCB are even today astonished to learn that every machine going through the assembly lines has a signed cheque lodged against it which is banked when the new machine leaves the factory gate. This way of doing things wasn't started by Mr Bamford, he merely copied what was done to him.

"In the early days we used to buy engine and transmission skid units from Ford six at a time. I would ring up and arrange to go there with the old Commer lorry and a trailer and they would always say 'now you'll be bringing a cheque with you, won't you?'. Quite rightly so. You don't go into a shop and expect to pay weeks later. I learned a lot from Ford."

Mr JCB believes that there has been great benefit to the company in making the dealer pay for the machine upon ex-works despatch:

"If the dealer has paid for it he will hustle and sell it and then order more. Let me tell you about the time I visited one of our dealers. There was a thrush nesting in a new generator outside and I enquired how he planned to solve the problem. He replied that as the generator was on consignment - at the manufacturer's expense - waiting a few more weeks before he could sell it didn't matter to him. I never forgot that."

As a youngster Joe Bamford moved around several companies to gain experience. He says that he had a 'broken apprenticeship' and proudly adds that he is entirely self taught. "I never passed an exam in my life". He did indeed work at the family company in Uttoxeter but just for little over a year.

1992. Mr JC Bamford's 75th Birthday was celebrated in Venice. Here he is with his two grandsons George, then ten years old, and Joseph Cyril II, then thirteen.

Looking back, it is easy to inject a romanticised view of the early years. This would be a distortion. The truth is that the hours were long and the work was hard. It is also easy to think of him as a man who always had all the answers.

"No, I did not have all the answers. But I was an enthusiast all the time. You see I have this thirst for knowledge."

Mr Bamford also talks frequently about goals. His first goal was to be better than Bamfords Ltd. To quantify this he took their turnover figure for parts business as a target.

"That was the figure I aimed at, I wanted to exceed it and I did. Of course I reserved the right to keep moving my goalposts. That's how I kept aiming higher."

Mr Bamford insists that his philosophies are 'all elementary stuff'. When he sees any mechanism for the first time he studies it carefully and begins counting.

"I always count the number of parts first. Generally I find that other people use more parts than I would. Parts are money. Better to keep it simple."

Never Look Back

Mr Bamford will only talk about the past in order to make a point for the future. The past as such doesn't interest him because he's always looking forward.

Praise has been heaped on the achievements of JCB and an easy focus has been to direct it to the man himself. Now is the time to put the record straight in several respects. He isn't over proud of what he has achieved so far because he has another goal - he wants to see JCB number two in the world, behind only the mighty Caterpillar.

"Our greatest moment hasn't been reached yet. I really do believe that we've only just started in business and there's a long way to go. To be number two in the world really will require a lot of hard work and dedication. It will be our biggest challenge."

He is proud of others. Of his son Anthony he says: "He is a much better manager than I was, and he is more commercially aware." As to his own shortcomings in business he admits to being several times tempted "to go off in all sorts of directions, which would have been wrong." It was others in his management team who he says rightly pulled back in favour of consolidating the business.

The man who gave his initials to the company and to the language praises others above himself.

"I helped, yes, but I didn't do it, the team did. It has been a team effort."

He believes that change is a stimulating factor. "You've got to be evolving every ten years and then starting again."

And yet there is something which he puts on an even higher plane than change. It is this - a sense of urgency.

Here's a classic Joe Bamford story: "We only bought three things on hire purchase, a Studebaker chassis and a lathe, although for some reason they sent two lathes instead of the one I ordered. The deal was through Bowmaker Finance. Years later I went to see them and they took me down into their cellar. They pulled from the archives a document from the time immediately before that purchase and it read 'J C Bamford. Crakemarsh. Little chance of expansion.' I wonder if they still have that?"

Mr Bamford was clearly amused. His first lathe is still in XP (the in-company term for Research and Development)

What did Mr JCB most look for in others ? "Enthusiasm". What did he most dislike in others : "A lack of interest, and you can find it in people at all levels and in all walks of life."

Of all the products through all the years, all the milestones and breakthroughs, what was the one which was most important to him ?

"The trailers. They were very economic to make and yet I made profit from them. It was sheer economic necessity and I learned such a lot from the experience. I couldn't have two parts where one would do ."

Many years ago he seized upon a comment by a Frenchman who had observed that he was never satisfied. "You are Jamais Content Bamford", the Frenchman remarked. Mr JCB was so tickled he has used it as his motto ever since.

He volunteered himself for one more question. "What else would you like to ask me?" he enquired.

This was the question. If you had to put simply what it is that makes JCB different from all the rest , what would you say ?

The answer was delivered immediately: "As before, my initials J.C. - Jamais Content - never content. That's totally true."

This 1987 edition of Collins Dictionary was the first to recognise JCB as a part of the English Language.
In 1989 JCB entered the Oxford English Dictionary, regarded as the most authoritative and comprehensive dictionary of English in the world. In it, the JCB entry reads:
"JCB: A proprietary name of excavators and other earth-moving equipment made by the firm of JC Bamford Excavators Ltd".

Joe and Anthony Bamford together in 1964.

Sir Anthony and Mr JC Bamford CBE in the JCB Reception Hall, February 1995.

Like Father, Like Son ?

Anthony Paul Bamford's childhood memories are inextricably bound to the company. On school holidays and at weekends he would be with his mother and father, and they would be with the business. So was he.

Joe Bamford went into business on the day Anthony was born. Anthony was there in his carry cot when his mother drove to the Black Country to buy supplies for production. He was there sitting beside John Wheeldon when John delivered machines to customers, or asleep on the bench seat of the company's first vehicle, an ex-army Dodge truck, as John collected components from suppliers.

He is the little boy standing on the gatepost next to Mr JCB in one of the earliest company photographs. When Mr Bamford discussed business with Sir Alfred Owen in his office at the huge Rubery Owen works in Darlaston, Anthony would be there. And when Mr Bamford, on a trip with chief designer Alec Kelly, spotted a clever hydraulic backhoe device in Norway in the early fifties, Anthony was there too.

"My father always involved me. He treated me like a grown up even in those early pioneering days," Anthony remembers. Being there as a boy in the presence of such giants of industry as Sir Alfred Owen gives Sir Anthony Bamford cause for reflection, for the huge Rubery Owen empire, from which JCB was to buy so much over the coming years, hardly exists today. The man who sits in the top office of the JCB empire understands how business must continually re-evaluate position and strength.

This fiftieth year marks that rarest of all activities at JCB, a time to look back. For this is a company only interested in tomorrow.

Anthony: "At fifty we can reflect and say we could not have done it without all those who have put much into this business. We are here because of so many, from the people who sweep the floors to those who design machines, make them and sell them. And I don't just include employees, there's the dealers and customers, and our suppliers too. Without this huge demonstration of loyalty and enthusiasm JCB wouldn't be what it is today."

The JCB culture is to travel hopefully but never actually arrive. Others looking in on the success of the huge Rocester plant, the factories of the new business units, and the subsidiary and associate companies and dealers worldwide, see a point of arrival. Anthony Bamford, head of the group of companies now employing 3,000 people sees only refuelling stops along the way.

During the period in which he has run the company, UK national manufacturing employment has dropped from 7.7m to 4.2m, and in the West Midlands from 1.1m to 562,000. In this same period the JCB workforce has doubled. JCB must be doing it right. It is not luck.

At JCB it has not been a matter of producing more of the same, but more of new or improved products within chosen markets.

Anthony: "We are ploughing our own furrow, chiefly in construction and agriculture. Very few of our major competitors are doing that, they're into all sorts of things. We stick to what we know, but at the same time we exude innovation. Our skill isn't in buying up businesses and turning them around, it is coming up with new products that customers want."

He is critical of big business which looks for growth through acquisition, rather than development. Anthony Bamford says he is not an engineer like his father. Yet since the late seventies JCB has extended its range to eight product groups. Today there are more than fifty different current models within those eight product groups. So for someone who is not an engineer, he has a keen appreciation of development engineering.

It is through this broad scope that Anthony will develop JCB, aiming at the goals which he has set for profit of £100m on sales of £1000m. This he calls a short term goal.

And Anthony complements all this with his appreciation and care for the environment at Rocester.

His concept of making the industrial working environment a place of beauty has been years ahead of its time. Today around the three man-made lakes there are 25 species of bird including rare black Australian swans. The lakes are richly stocked for anglers.

A striking sculpture park was begun in the late seventies by the building of the Fossor - Latin for digger - a 70 tonne creation by Wylenty Pytel. There are also two works by local sculptor Mark Delf, Startled Horse and Opus - which shows men digging and embodies the theme of team spirit.

Thousands of visitors come to admire the landscaped setting and to picnic by the lakes. Anthony says: "Factories do not have to be in mean city streets, they can be exuberant, living in harmony with the countryside."

Over the years JCB has given quietly and generously to charities and to the neighbourhood. It is the company policy to be a good neighbour and the village of Rocester has benefitted from JCB's positive actions.

The parish church has a new spire and vestry, and the village itself is being redeveloped thanks to a gift of four acres of land from JCB which has enabled the village centre to be re-developed, so putting the heart back into a place which can trace its history back to a Roman settlement. It was JCB which sponsored a competition to find the best architect for the job.

The company has also embraced the Staffordshire community by sponsoring a photographic competition entitled the Spirit of Staffordshire in which photographers were invited to capture the essential quality of the county.

In this Golden Jubilee year JCB is sponsoring a competition to find Staffordshire's most caring community in an award scheme which uniquely brings together private industry, the local authority, a charity and the Church. The Bishop of Lichfield is Chairman of the judging panel.

It is also the centenary of the mid-Staffordshire Branch of the NSPCC, of which Lady Bamford is President. The work force decided to organise a large number of fund raising projects for the Society, including a grand open day at the Rocester factory on June 10 for more than 20,000 people.

There are many other acts of sponsorship and kindness that the company and employees quietly organise.

One current example is a 45 foot 9 tonne all steel narrow boat which is being custom-built in a section of the ram tube stores by a number of employees to take disabled children for trips on the Cheddleton to Froghall canal. The Lady B will be operational in late 1995.

Against these charitable actions Anthony weighs up the future of the business.

The longer term challenge is to be the pre-eminent manufacturer in Europe, to stand against Caterpillar in the USA and Komatsu in Japan. All this is an ambitious way forward, stemming from growth through innovation. It's all a long way from his first day as the boss when he walked in apprehensively.

"I really was quite scared, and there have also been other days when I've felt that way too. But I had been well prepared by my father and he was wise to do so. Also we had a very good team around us when I took over, people like Gilbert Johnston and Dick Ryeland."

Johnston was soon to be chief executive and Ryeland managing director of JCB Sales Ltd.

Anthony has found business to be immensely enjoyable: "I think a lot of people here do enjoy moving forward and taking on the challenges. It's made better people of them. They have been surprised at what they have made possible, and been able to achieve."

Divisionalisation has worked at JCB, providing a focus dictated by product group. He agrees that product focus before divisionalisation had its highs and lows. Partly this was due to the company's traditional focus on the backhoe loader range. This is still the number one product and Anthony sees

great potential in making the concept accepted in those world markets where it has hitherto not been strong.

He also sees potential in established markets through improving the backhoe loader still further by an increasing focus on comfort and ease of operator control. But now the other business units are free to develop, often with products in competition with conventional backhoe loaders produced at Rocester. Anthony: "The challenge is always there. In business you can never relax".

The JCB approach to innovation is what he calls "ideas within a theme." One example is the unique 1CX compact backhoe which was developed from an idea during development of the JCB Robot skid steer loader.

"There is nothing in that product which is new in engineering terms, and yet it shows how engineering innovation can be applied. It is this which makes us world class".

It is often said that Anthony is not like his father, and he is the first to agree that this is true. "I have never tried to emulate him, indeed that would be impossible. But I do of course admire him immensely for what he has achieved. My father's thrust was engineering and I couldn't have evolved the business that he did. But I'm just as interested in the new

products even though I'm not a qualified engineer."

In the early seventies Anthony showed his ability to focus on business issues, and one of the best examples of this was his work with Gilbert Johnston establishing JCB's wholly-owned subsidiary JCB France in 1972.

Anthony with Gilbert Johnston on the tracked excavator production line in 1985.

Decision making is something JCB is good at because it is prepared to invest in potential. Anthony : "The thrust into exporting has been vital. Where would we be today without our export business ? And yet we don't believe in an instant return. Look at our company in North America, which we supported for over 12 years before we began to see a return. But now North America is a very successful market for us.

Decision making is important and its very satisfying to see things come to fruition years afterwards. Particularly when there are risks attached."

Anthony celebrates the achievements of the past, but does not look back to any golden age.
"These fifty years have not been easy, but for most of the people involved they have been enthralling and exhilarating, and the business wouldn't be here today without the efforts of all those people."

This praise is not to be confused with any clinging on to the past. "The worst thing is to look back. Its dangerous to look back."

In 1982 JCB built the 100,000th machine, a 3CX backhoe loader. It took just a further nine years to reach the 200,000th machine in 1991 and the 250,000th machine was manufactured in 1995. So JCB cannot be accused of looking back. There is no golden age set in the past. The best is yet to be.

Anthony believes that family run businesses have great advantages over public companies.

"The strongest contribution is continuity. People know who the boss is and what the values are, and they can see the continuity down the years. I am the second generation and I certainly hope that there will be a third generation to take the business forward.

This company will provide employment for future generations because we know where we are going, we know the market place, and we have the right products."

On a visit with his father to Norway in 1956, young Anthony was pictured with this Fordson Major fitted with JCB Half Tracks, a successful export to Scandinavia.

In 1990 Anthony Bamford was created Knight Bachelor in The Queen's Birthday Honours List. Sir Anthony is here pictured after his investiture with his wife Carole and their daughter Alice outside Buckingham Palace.

Three mile factory walk.

10,000 visitors a year come to Lakeside Works, and they are shown around by retired employees known as the JCB Redcoats. Reg Williams (centre front row) joined JCB in 1959 and spent most of his career in the demonstration team. Now he is full time visits officer and brings in the tour guides as required.

The full three mile factory tour is at least a two and a half hour hike.

Pictured in the reception hall are (standing, left to right) Bert West who clocked up 31 years full time service. Bert died in February. Roy Pattinson 19 years, John Chandler 30, John Wheeldon 42 years service and founder member, Arthur Morfitt 26, Alf Bettany 25, Cyril Keeling 28. (front row) Alf Keates 26, Reg Williams 36 to date, Jim Rowlinson 10 years.

The company's seven earliest employees who remained loyal during the formative years are referred to as founder members, and a special tie was awarded to each in the late 1960's. Founder members are Bill Hirst MBE, John Wheeldon, Don Wood MBE and Bernard Archer. Also the late Arthur Harrison, Alec Hollingworth and Arthur Ratcliffe.

Don Wood, who joined in August 1951, is now the only founder member still in full time employment. He has spent many years in JCB Research and is now a cell manager supplying services to JCB group companies.

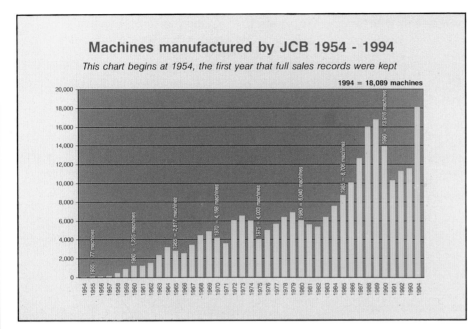

Machines manufactured by JCB 1954 - 1994

This chart begins at 1954, the first year that full sales records were kept

1994 = 18,089 machines

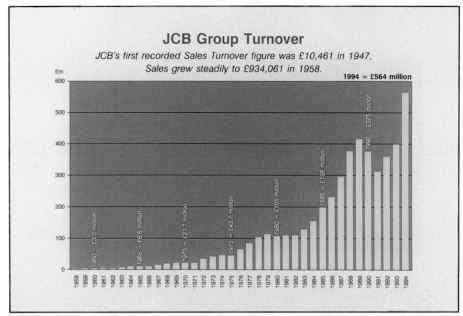

JCB Group Turnover

JCB's first recorded Sales Turnover figure was £10,461 in 1947.
Sales grew steadily to £934,061 in 1958.

1994 = £564 million

These graphs demonstrate JCB's remarkable growth over the years.

In 1994 sales were £564m, a dramatic increase of 42% on the previous year. Of those £564m sales, £140m came from products launched within the past five years, showing true incremental business and underlining the value of investment during recession.

Each employee's work was worth 6.5 machines to the company, a striking example of productivity.

JCB exports more than 60% and is now one of the world's largest and most successful construction equipment groups, poised to play an even larger part in the developing markets of Latin America, the Far East including India, and China.

JCB AWARDS

Anthony Bamford with the Duke of Edinburgh, July 1981.
The Queen's Award to Industry for Export Achievement was
presented here in the JCB theatre.

Mark Bamford, director, with Mrs J C Bamford in 1984
receiving the Royal Agricultural Society's certificate of merit
from Mrs Anne Armstrong, former Ambassador to the Court
of St James, who opened the Royal Show. The certificate
was awarded to the JCB 410 Farm Master.

1969   J C Bamford appointed Commander of
        the British Empire.

        Queen's Award to Industry for Export
        Achievement. J C Bamford Excavators.

1973   Design Council Award for Technological
        design.
        J C Bamford Excavators.

        European Gold Mercury Award for
        Technological design.
        J C Bamford Excavators.

1974   Queen's Award to Industry.
        JCB Research.

        Queen's Award to Industry. JCB Sales.

1975   Design Council Award for Technological
        Design.
        J C Bamford Excavators.

1976   SM 'Bill' Hirst, service director, awarded
        MBE for services to British exports.

1979   Young Businessman of the Year.
        The Guardian newspaper.
        A P Bamford.

        Queen's Award to Industry for Export
        Achievement, JCB Sales.

        Royal Society of Arts Presidential Award
        for consistent distinguished design
        policy.

        Business and Industry Awards. Premier
        award for human and social
        responsibility and environmental quality.

1981   Queen's Award to Industry for Export
        Achievement. JCB Service.

        Leipzig Spring Fair. Gold medal for
        outstanding quality.

1982   Royal Agricultural Society of England
        and the Royal Society for the Prevention
        of Accidents.
        JCB Materials Handling.

        Don Wood, JCB Research awarded MBE.

1983   Pierre Leboucher, managing director JCB
        France, awarded OBE for services to
        British exports

        The Royal Show. The Robert Barrow
        Award for the most outstanding
        machinery demonstration.

1984   Queen's Award to Industry for Export
        Achievement.
        JCB Materials Handling.

        Institute of Marketing. National
        marketing awards for outstanding
        achievement in British marketing,
        JCB Sales Ltd.

        British Quality Award for exceptional
        improvements in the quality of a
        product. For 3CX service, maintenance
        and support.

        Design Council Award for the JCB 3CX
        Backhoe Loader designed by:
        Derek Prime, Roy Allsopp, Ted Hulse,
        Brian Hague, Alan Walker, John Hassall,
        Mick Higgs.

1985   J C Bamford, Doctor of Technology,
        Loughborough University.

        British Quality Award. For outstanding
        achievement in product design quality
        and implementation of new and
        imaginative quality assurance methods.

1987 A P Bamford appointed Hon. Master of Engineering, University of Birmingham.

General Aviation Manufacturers and Traders Association award for efficient and profitable use of business aircraft for the benefit of the company.
JCB Aviation.

1988 A P Bamford appointed Hon. Doctor of University of Keele for services to industry.
Queen's Award to Industry for Export Achievement.

Roger Eve, President JCB Inc. awarded OBE for services to British exports.

Britain's Best Factories Award, Management Today magazine, for world-class manufacturing facilities.

1989 A P Bamford awarded Chevalier de L'Ordre National du Merité for significant progress achieved by the company in France over 15 years.

A P Bamford, Individual Leadership award, PA Consulting Group Midlands.

Royal Agricultural Society of England. The Burke Trophy for outstanding contribution to mechanisation.

British Association of Landscape Industries award for the JCB roof garden.

Premier Environment Award, Business and Industry Commitment to the Environment Panel, for outstanding achievement in environmental care.

1990 A P Bamford created Knight Bachelor in the Queen's Birthday Honours.

Premier Award for outstanding marketing achievement, with the JCB Loadall. Institute of Marketing.

Financial Times and London Business School design management award.

Machinery Award for innovation in production engineering.
JCB Transmissions.

1991 J C Bamford, Doctor of Business Administration, Board of International Management Centres.

Engineering Maintenance Award.
JCB Transmissions.

Bernard 'Ranji' Bullock awarded the BEM. He joined JCB in 1957 and retired from the Ram Shop in 1994.

1992 J C Bamford, Degree of Engineering, Sheffield University, in recognition of outstanding contribution to innovative engineering.

A P Bamford made Fellow of the City & Guilds Institute of London.

British Design Council Award for design of the Fastrac. JCB Landpower.

Gold Medal, Fieragricola, Italy, for the JCB Fastrac. JCB Landpower.

Gilbert Johnston awarded CBE.

1993 J C Bamford becomes only Briton honoured in Construction Equipment Hall of Fame, USA.

Corporate Video of the Year, Royal Television Society Midlands Centre.
JCB Landpower.

1994 A P Bamford appointed Hon Fellow Chartered Society of Designers; also Hon Doctor Science, University of Cranfield.

Queen's Award for Technological Achievement.
JCB Backhoe Loader Division.

Queen's Award for Export Achievement.
JCB Hydrapower.

Silver Medal, Machinery Award Scheme, Royal Agricultural Society of England. For the JCB Fastrac. JCB Landpower.

1995 JCB Landpower awarded 1994 Prince of Wales Award for Innovation for development of the JCB Fastrac.
Presented on BBC1 Tomorrow's World programme.

Prince Charles meets JCB employees, November 1977.

Anthony Bamford, Prince Michael of Kent, Derek Danson, touring the factory in April 1983.

Anthony Bamford with Margaret Thatcher and her husband Denis on a factory visit to JCB at Rocester in June 1987.

Anthony Bamford with The Princess Royal, who opened the new showroom and office complex in June 1989.

Anthony and Mrs Marjorie Bamford with the Duke of Kent, November 1977.

Roy Harrison, calibration engineer, and Michelle Roberts, talk to The Princess Royal on her visit in June 1989. Production director Reg Hooper is on the right.

Derek Prime, Prince Michael of Kent, Don Wood, Dick Ryeland, and Anthony Bamford, April 1983.

Mr J C Bamford CBE with Her Majesty The Queen at the Chelsea Flower Show, May 1993, discussing the JCB Robot and the new yellow rose 'Mr JCB'.

Alice Bamford meets the Duchess of Kent, July 1986.

At 10 Downing Street in September 1988 with Prime Minister Margaret Thatcher, the presentation of the JCB N.S.P.C.C. workforce appeal cheque for £250,000. This was an appeal year to benefit the Mid Staffordshire Branch of the N.S.P.C.C. and the money went to Carole House, a new child care centre at Tunstall. The workforce raised £125,000 which was doubled by Anthony Bamford. Left to right: Max Woolley, Kim Dudley, Anthony and Carole Bamford, John Atkinson, John Sandland, Margaret Thatcher, Pat Smith, Ken Horleston, Mike Lee, Cynthia Woolley, Ivy Taylor.

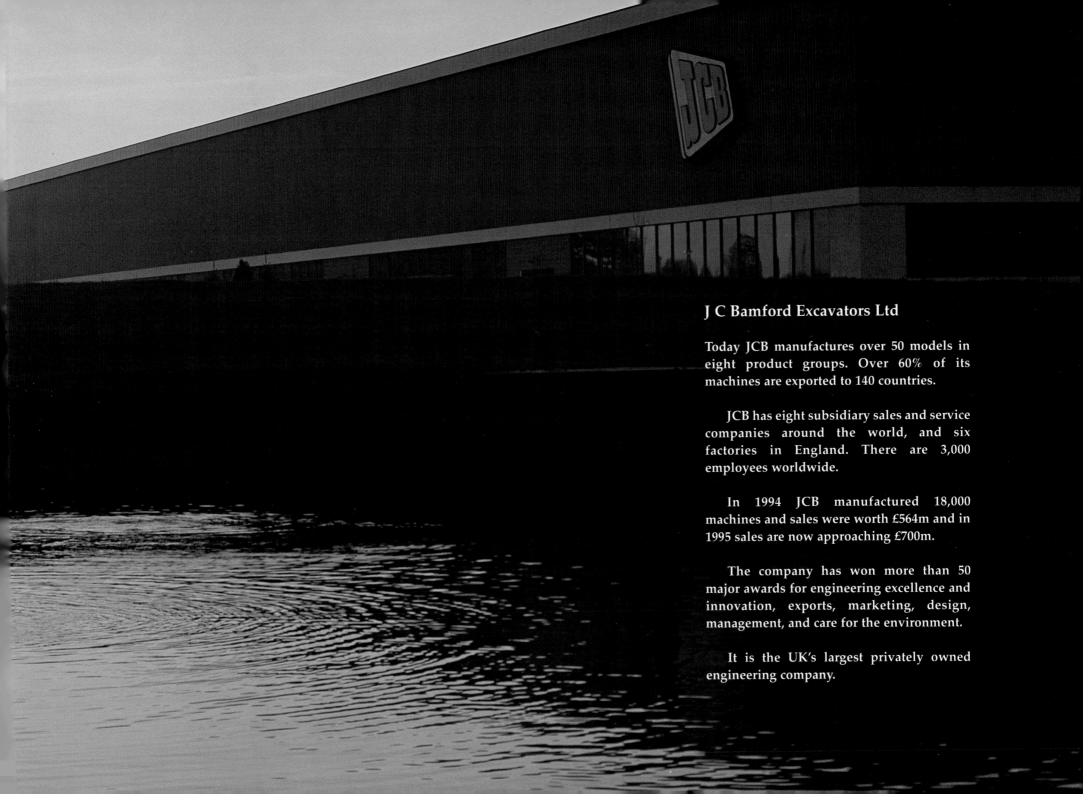

J C Bamford Excavators Ltd

Today JCB manufactures over 50 models in eight product groups. Over 60% of its machines are exported to 140 countries.

JCB has eight subsidiary sales and service companies around the world, and six factories in England. There are 3,000 employees worldwide.

In 1994 JCB manufactured 18,000 machines and sales were worth £564m and in 1995 sales are now approaching £700m.

The company has won more than 50 major awards for engineering excellence and innovation, exports, marketing, design, management, and care for the environment.

It is the UK's largest privately owned engineering company.

J C Bamford Excavators Limited,
Rocester, Staffordshire ST14 5JP
Great Britain.

Telephone: 01889 590312
Facsimile: 01889 590588

JCB Part No. 9999 / 2957